HEINEMANN
ADVANCED
SCIENCE

Medical Physics: Imaging

JEAN POPE

Heinemann

HOW TO USE THIS BOOK

Heinemann Advanced Science: Medical Physics: Imaging has been written to support medical physics options, in particular that offered by Edexcel. It contains all the material covered by that syllabus, namely the major imaging techniques as well as radiotherapy. The book also meets the medical imaging requirements of other examination boards.

The style of the book is similar to that of the core book, *Heinemann Advanced Science: Physics*. In addition to the main text, there are three different types of boxes.

- The blue tinted *information boxes* contain important information that you need to know.
- The pink headed *extension boxes* present more advanced information, which can be addressed when you have come to grips with the basic text material.
  These boxes need not interfere with your reading and understanding of the main text, and can be returned to when you are ready.
- At the end of each major topic within a chapter, you will find a green *key points box*. This is designed to assist you not only to digest the material you have just covered, but also with your revision.

Throughout the book, there are *worked examples*. These should help to cement your understanding of, and ability to apply, the basic principles, and they form an important part of the learning process. In addition, there is a wide selection of questions at the end of each chapter, to help you find out how much of the chapter you have really understood.

To go with the book there is a web page which contains a brief introduction to the imaging techniques that are taking us into the twenty-first century. They are not required (yet!) by A-level examination syllabuses, but no medical imaging book would be complete without a glimpse at the state-of-the-art imaging systems. Indeed, the whole field of medical imaging is progressing so fast that who knows what we shall be 'seeing' in the next century. References to the web page are made in the text as (see Web page). The Web page address is http://www.heinemann.co.uk/science

Acknowledgements

So many people have helped with the preparation of this book that it is difficult to know where to start with my thanks. For expert medical advice, the 'team' at the Department of Medical Physics and Bioengineering, University College London, has been invaluable. Alan Cottenden and his colleagues Professor Roland Blackwell, Peter Marsden, Mike Mooney, Professor Roger Ordidge, Sean Smart, Alison Vinall and Wendy Waddington have all been extremely helpful and encouraging, reading chapters and giving me their comments. At Derriford Hospital, here in Plymouth, Nick Ring, Paul Ormsby and Ivor Jones have provided me with valuable advice as well as illustrations.

A special thanks also to Lindsey Charles, Clare Farley, Donna Evans and Leigh Hicks at Heinemann, for their patience and efficiency in bringing this book to publication. Patrick Fullick too has made an enormous contribution through his advice on style and content.

The home 'team', Chris, Vicky, Nick and David, have also offered the skills so typical of their generation. These ranged from expert computer advice to providing personal X-rays and MRI scans through various sports injuries!

Finally, my mentor! Without the constant support of my husband Roger, who never doubted it would be done, the book would not yet be off the hard drive.

Jean Pope September 1998

Dedication

For my mother, who would have loved to have seen the finished book.

CONTENTS

INTRODUCTION

Medical imaging

A century ago, the only way a doctor could see inside your body was through surgery. Today, as you pass through the automatic doors of a modern hospital, you are in a different world. Now, without the use of a scalpel, not only is there a non-invasive way of 'seeing' the structure and function of every part of your complicated anatomy, but also, your doctors have the choice of **four** *possible imaging techniques at their disposal (figure I.1). Each of these techniques, or* **modalities**, *has its own special advantages.*

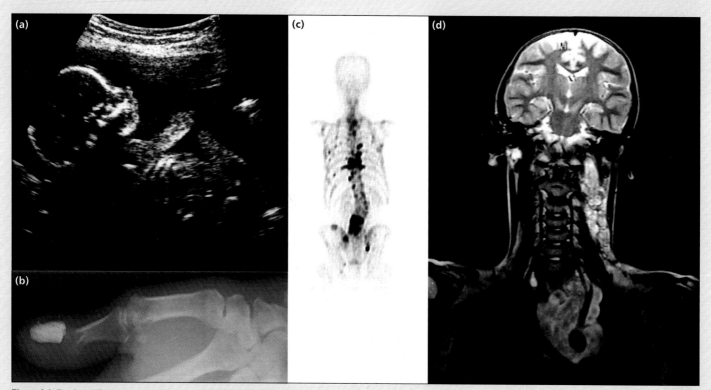

Figure I.1 The four different imaging techniques: **(a)** an ultrasound scan of an unborn baby; **(b)** an X-ray of a factory worker's thumb that had been badly crushed in an accident. Doctors used bone cells taken from the patient's arm to grow and then transplant the missing thumb tip. **(c)** nuclear medicine – a bone scan showing cancer (black regions) as well as, collapsed vertebrae and distortion of the spine; **(d)** a magnetic resonance image (MRI) showing wonderful detail of the head and neck.

An '**X-ray**', (with its sophisticated off-shoot of Computed Tomography – CT for short), is still the first course of action if you report to the casualty department with a suspected broken ankle. A clear image of your bone structure is acquired in minutes, and a diagnosis can be made.

Ultrasound, however, will be the department towards which most pregnant women entering a hospital will be heading. Using pulses of very high frequency sound, the doctor will be able to display on a screen a squirming, kicking baby for all the family to see, long before it is born. The method is the safest one known by which to image the vulnerable unborn child.

Nuclear medicine offers us something completely different. By administering a radioactive tracer to the patient, its passage through the body can be monitored, to yield information about how the system is *working*. It can show, for example, how cancer may be spreading from its primary site to other parts of the body.

Finally, there is **Magnetic Resonance Imaging** or **MRI**. This, the most recent addition to the imaging tools, is perhaps the most complex. The patient is placed in an incredibly strong magnet, the heart of the machine, providing a field more than 10 000 times greater than that of the Earth's magnetic field. A radio frequency pulse is sent in for a short time and then turned off. The patient's response to this pulse is monitored and the information is used to construct an internal image.

Despite the high cost of such machines, the detail they can provide in images of joints and soft tissues is unrivalled.

It is impossible to say which modality is 'the best'. They all have their strengths and weaknesses, just like any member of a team, and indeed that is what they are – an imaging team. The following table summarises some of their good and bad points, but the important thing to remember is that they can be used in conjunction with each other.

Perhaps the most exciting prospect for the future is a combination of all the various imaging techniques to give '**multimodality**' displays. Such combined imaging would draw the best features from each mode and make them truly *complementary*.

Table I.1 A comparison of the main medical imaging modalities.

	X-RAYS	CT	ULTRASOUND	NUCLEAR	MRI
bone	the preferred technique, giving the best resolution	used for more complicated structures	poor – ultrasound will not penetrate bone	good for **early** diagnosis, (e.g. of stress fractures), and whole body bone cancer	gives weak MRI signal, so restricted use
brain and spinal cord	radiograph of limited use	good and preferred to MRI for bony spine details	poor – difficult to image through the skull without surgery	poor – improved quality with PET scans	excellent – the preferred option in most cases, giving good contrast
chest	radiograph gives adequate routine lung screening	CT preferred for better detail	poor – ultrasound cannot image past air spaces	very good for functional studies of both air and blood flow	little used – MRI not good for imaging air spaces
heart and circulation	needs contrast medium	limited use – recent advances with digital imaging techniques	excellent – the preferred technique in many cases. Velocities, (Doppler), as well as structure analysed	flow studies useful	good resolution capabilities and increasing in popularity
soft tissues (joints)	radiograph gives poor contrast	good and preferred to MRI for extra bone details	reasonable, although bone blocks ultrasound	resolution poor, but gives functional information	excellent – the preferred method for studying muscle, tendons, cartilage etc.
soft tissues (abdomen)	radiograph poor and needs contrast medium	useful for whole abdomen scan	excellent – by far the preferred choice in obstetrics, since safe and real-time imaging	useful functional study of liver, kidneys etc and growth of tumours	little used at present, but good resolution for specified areas
comfort and safety	radiograph gives small radiation dose	high dose	no known hazards	moderate dose due to administered radionuclides	pacemakers, implants etc. a hazard. Some claustrophobia
examination time	very fast	moderate	moderate	can be lengthy, waiting for tracer distribution	long
spatial resolution	0.1 mm	0.25 mm	1–5 mm	5–15 mm	0.3–1 mm
mobility	small portable machines available	none	portable machines widely used	none	very limited
capital cost	£50 k (low)	£500 k (quite high)	£10–150 k (moderate)	£100–400 k (quite high)	£1–2 million (very high)
cost per image	£50–300	£150	£50–100	£100–500	£200–400

The preferred techniques in particular areas are indicated by shading, but all the features will be discussed in the chapters that follow.

Ultrasound

You will almost certainly have noticed that if you shout loudly in the direction of a distant wall, you hear an echo of your voice shortly afterwards, as the sound waves bounce off the wall and return to your ear. You may also have noticed that the further away you are from the wall, the longer it takes for your echo to return to you.

These simple observations form the basis of **echo (or depth) sounding**, in which the position of an object is estimated by measuring the time taken for echoes to return from it. In order to produce accurate information about the surface reflecting the sound waves, we must minimise the 'spread' of the sound waves as they diffract around obstacles in their path. Since waves with high frequencies are diffracted less than waves with low frequencies, echo-sounding uses sound waves with very high frequencies, called **ultrasound**.

Figure 1.1 A variety of ultrasound scans may be used to image different structures of the body. Here, the A-scan gives dimensions in the eye, a Doppler investigation yields information about moving structures in the heart, and the B-scan provides a picture of an unborn baby.

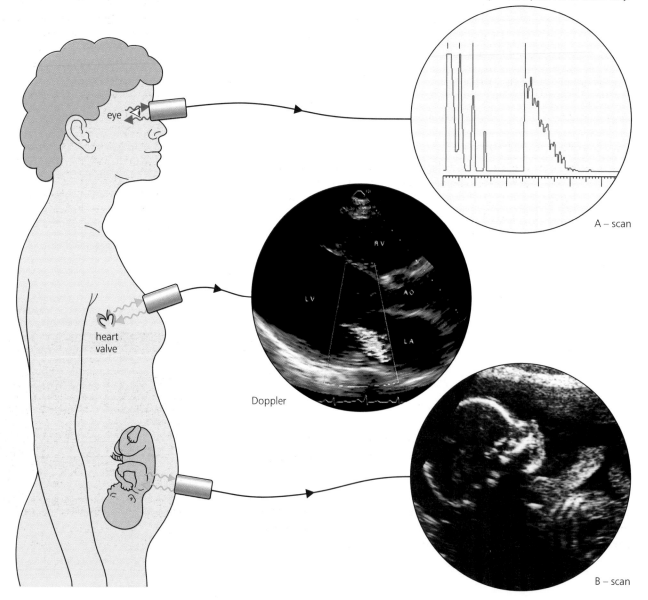

eye

A – scan

heart valve

Doppler

B – scan

Over the years, ultrasound has seen many applications. It has been exploited by warships to detect the presence of submarines, by fishermen to locate shoals of fish beneath their boats, by oceanographers to chart the contours of the seabed, and by doctors to 'see' into the body (figure 1.1). This last application forms the subject of this chapter.

Back in the 1960s, doctors already knew that ultrasound scanning provided a safe, reliable way of 'observing' babies in their mothers' wombs. Since then, ultrasound imaging of the body has come a long way. Using up-to-date engineering technology and state-of-the art computers, it is now possible to view highly detailed two- and three-dimensional images, in 'real time', and so watch a baby as it kicks and squirms only a few weeks after conception. With many uses, other than pre-natal scanning, ultrasound is now a widely used medical imaging technique (or 'modality'), second only to conventional X-rays in popularity.

ULTRASOUND AND ITS PRODUCTION

Ultrasonic sound waves, or ultrasound, are high-frequency sound waves above the human ear's audible range: that is with a frequency greater than 20 kHz.

In fact, the frequencies used in medicine are much higher than this, typically between 1 and 15 MHz (although even higher frequencies, up to 50 MHz, are used in specialised investigations).

Like all sound waves, ultrasound consists of longitudinal, elastic or pressure waves, capable of travelling through solids, liquids and gases. This makes them ideal for penetrating the body, unlike transverse mechanical waves, which cannot travel to any great extent through fluids.

How is ultrasound produced?

Ultrasound is both generated and detected through high-frequency oscillations in **piezoelectric crystals**. These materials are capable of interchanging mechanical and electrical energy through the **piezoelectric effect** (figure 1.2). The most common piezoelectric material used in medicine is the synthetic ceramic, lead zirconate titanate (PZT).

Tranducers

A **transducer** is a device for converting one type of signal into another. For instance, the eye is an optical transducer, changing incoming light waves into electrical pulses to the brain; a thermometer is a temperature transducer, translating temperature changes into, for example, volume changes of mercury; the ear is an acoustic transducer, converting sound inputs into electrical signals.

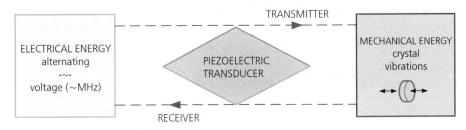

Figure 1.2 Energy conversions in a piezoelectric transducer.

A tiny (0.4 mm thick), piezoelectric element is incorporated into a **piezoelectric transducer**, and formed into a hand-held **probe** (figure 1.3). This can then operate as:

- an ultrasound transmitter, by applying a stimulating voltage of suitable frequency, thus making the crystal vibrate and emit ultrasonic waves
- an ultrasound receiver, by monitoring the piezoelectric voltage developed across the crystal when it is forced to vibrate by returning ultrasonic echoes.

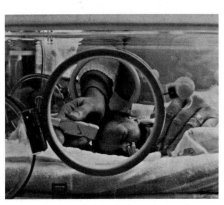

Figure 1.3 An ultrasound probe is used to acquire an image of the brain of the new born baby.

The Piezoelectric effect

The basis of the piezoelectric effect is the slight rearrangement of charges within a stressed piezoelectric material. In an unstressed state, the centres of symmetry of both the positive and negative ions of such a crystal lattice coincide and no effective charge appears on electrodes attached to the crystal (figure 1.4(a)). However, when the crystal is compressed or extended (figure 1.4(b) and (c)), the centres of symmetry move, no longer coincide, and give rise to free charges on the electrodes, thus producing a voltage across them. If the crystal is forced to vibrate, an alternating voltage then appears across it.

Conversely, if a voltage is applied across an unstressed piezoelectric crystal, the centres of symmetry move, hence deforming the crystal. An applied alternating voltage thus gives rise to mechanical vibrations in the crystal, or a single voltage pulse sets the crystal 'ringing' like an electronic gong, emitting a burst of ultrasound waves. Maximum response (or resonance) occurs when the applied frequency matches a natural frequency of vibration of the crystal. The fundamental mode occurs when opposite faces of the crystal are antinodes of the stationary wave set up, with a single node in the middle (figure 1.4(d)).

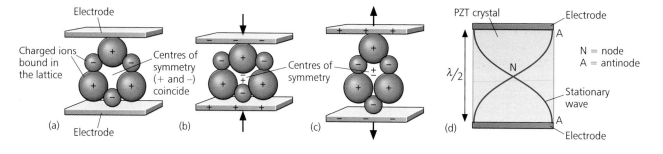

Figure 1.4 The piezoelectric crystal: **(a)** unstressed; **(b)** compressed; **(c)** extended; **(d)** stationary wave in the crystal.

Resonance in a piezoelectric crystal – Worked example

A fundamental resonance occurs in a piezoelectric crystal when its thickness is equal to $\lambda/2$ where λ is the wavelength of the resulting ultrasonic waves. Find the frequency of the ultrasound emitted from a PZT element of thickness 0.38 mm, given that the velocity of ultrasound in PZT is 3800 m s^{-1}. Explain in terms of stationary waves why $\lambda/2$ is the chosen thickness.

The fundamental wavelength λ is double the element thickness, i.e.

$$\lambda = 2 \times 0.38 \, \text{mm}$$
$$= 0.76 \, \text{mm}$$

The frequency is found by applying the formula, $c = f\lambda$

$$f = \frac{c}{\lambda}$$
$$= \frac{3800 \, \text{m s}^{-1}}{0.76 \times 10^{-3} \, \text{m}}$$
$$= 5 \times 10^{6} \, \text{Hz}$$
$$= 5 \, \text{MHz}$$

The outer edges of the crystal in contact with the electrodes must be antinodes for maximum response, and thus the simplest stationary wave pattern that can be set up is as shown in figure 1.4(d). For this reason, thin crystals are required for high-frequency generation.

THE INTERACTION OF ULTRASOUND WITH TISSUES

When ultrasound travels through any medium it is **attenuated**. When it meets the boundary between two media it can be **reflected** or **transmitted** (figure 1.5).

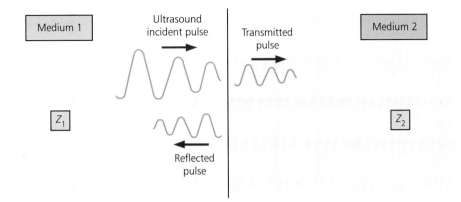

Figure 1.5 When ultrasound meets a boundary, it can be reflected or transmitted.

Attenuation of ultrasound

The **attenuation** of a wave describes the reduction in its intensity as it travels through a medium. This loss is due to a number of factors. The wave:

• simply *'spreads out'* and suffers an 'inverse square law type' reduction in intensity
• is *scattered* away from its original direction
• is *absorbed* in the medium.

The amount of **absorption** of an ultrasound beam in a medium (described by the absorption coefficient, a, in table 1.1) depends firstly on the type of medium. You can see from the table that whilst water absorbs very little ultrasound, bone is a strong absorber, putting it at risk, for example, during high-power ultrasound therapy.

Secondly, higher frequencies suffer greater absorption. (Listen to next door's music through the wall and hear the base notes dominate!) In fact, if the frequency is doubled, the absorption increases by a factor of four. This has very important consequences when choosing the best frequency at which to image the body. If the selected frequency is too high, the ultrasound will not be able to penetrate to the regions under investigation.

Table 1.1 Ultrasound in biological materials.

Medium	Density (ρ) (kg m^{-3})	Ultrasound velocity (c) (m s^{-1})	Specific acoustic impedance Z ($= \rho c$) (kg m^{-2} s^{-1})	Absorption coefficient a at 1 MHz (dB cm^{-1})
air	1.3	330	429	12
water	1000	1430	1.43×10^6	0.002
blood	1060	1570	1.59×10^6	0.2
brain	1025	1540	1.58×10^6	0.9
fat	952	1450	1.38×10^6	0.6
muscle (average)	1075	1590	1.70×10^6	2.3
soft tissue (average)	1060	1540	1.63×10^6	1.0
bone (varies)	1400 to 1908	4080	5.6×10^6 to 7.78×10^6	13

Absorption and the decibel scale

As an ultrasound beam travels through a medium, its intensity does not decrease by equal amounts for each millimetre travelled. This is because the absorption in each millimetre depends on what intensity is arriving there. The greater the incident intensity, the greater is the energy absorbed in that millimetre of the medium. Instead, it is the *fractional reduction* in intensity that remains the same for each millimetre travelled, resulting in a *logarithmic loss* in ultrasound intensity. This loss is characterised by an absorption coefficient, *a*, and is most conveniently measured using the logarithmic **decibel scale**.

The **decibel** is a unit of the intensity level of a sound. It is defined using base 10 logarithms, such that the difference in intensity level between two sounds of intensities I_1 and I_2 is given by

$$\textbf{difference in intensity level} = 10\log_{10}\left(\frac{I_2}{I_1}\right) \textbf{ dB}$$

where I_1 is the original intensity, and I_2 is the final value.

For example, using the average value of $1.0\,\text{dB cm}^{-1}$ for the average absorption of ultrasound in soft tissue from table 1.1, an ultrasound beam will suffer a loss in intensity of 30 dB in traversing 30 cm of soft tissue. A 30 dB loss implies that

$$10\log\left(\frac{I_2}{I_1}\right) = -30 \qquad \textbf{(the minus indicates a loss)}$$

$$\therefore\ \log\left(\frac{I_2}{I_1}\right) = -3$$

$$\therefore\ \left(\frac{I_2}{I_1}\right) = 10^{-3}$$

$$\therefore\ I_2 = \frac{I_1}{1000}$$

so the intensity of the beam is reduced by a factor of 1000.

Specific acoustic impedance

A medium tends to oppose the passage of sound waves through it, rather like an electrical circuit resists the flow of current through it. Just as the term electrical impedance is employed in the case of electricity, **acoustic impedance** is used to describe the opposition of a medium to the flow of sound waves. It is a measure of the way the molecules of the medium move in response to the acoustic pressure. It does not, however, describe the loss of energy of the wave to the medium; this is absorption. It rather relates to the acoustic 'match' of the wave to the medium: is the sound wave 'in the right gear' for efficient transmission?

The **specific acoustic impedance Z** of a medium is given by:

$$Z = \rho c \qquad \textbf{(1.1)}$$

where ρ is the density of the medium and c is the velocity of sound in it. Table 1.1 shows values of Z for common body materials. Notice how

$$Z_{\textbf{gas}} \ll Z_{\textbf{liquid}} < Z_{\textbf{solid}}$$

ULTRASOUND WAVES

- Have frequencies $>20\,\text{kHz}$ (medical use: **1–15 MHz**).
- Are **longitudinal** (can travel through body fluids).
- Meet opposition to their flow, described by the **specific acoustic impedance, $Z = \rho c$.**
- **Attenuation** is the reduction in wave intensity as it passes through a medium (higher frequencies are attenuated more).
- **Piezoelectric transducers** interchange electrical and mechanical energy, and are used to both generate and detect ultrasound.

Reflection of ultrasound

When a pulse of ultrasound is sent into the body and meets a boundary between two media, of different specific acoustic impedance Z, the sound wave needs to 'change gear' in order to continue. If the difference in Z across the boundary is large, the wave cannot easily adjust: there is an 'acoustic mismatch'. Most of the wave is thus reflected, and a strong echo is recorded. If, however, there is an 'acoustic match' between the media, most of the wave is transmitted, resulting in good penetration, but a weak echo.

The fraction of the intensity reflected back (I_r) to that incident (I_i), at normal incidence, is known as the **intensity reflection coefficient**, α

$$\alpha = \frac{I_r}{I_i}$$

which in turn is given by

$$\alpha = \frac{(Z_2 - Z_1)^2}{(Z_2 + Z_1)^2} \qquad (1.2)$$

Large differences in Z give rise to large values for α, producing strong echoes.

Reflection at a body interface – Worked example

Choosing suitable values from table 1.1, estimate the percentage of incident intensity reflected back at a fat/muscle boundary.

We need to calculate the value of α for the boundary using equation 1.2:

$$\alpha = \frac{(Z_2 - Z_1)^2}{(Z_2 + Z_1)^2}$$

From table 1.1, $Z_1 = 1.38 \times 10^6$ kg m^{-2} s^{-1} (fat) and $Z_2 = 1.70 \times 10^6$ kg m^{-2} s^{-1} (muscle)

$$\alpha = \frac{(1.70 - 1.38)^2}{(1.70 + 1.38)^2}$$

$$= 0.011$$

(The units all cancel and α is dimensionless.)
Hence, 1.1 % of the incident intensity is reflected back.

Table 1.2 shows the typical range of α-values encountered at various body interfaces.

Table 1.2 Reflection coefficients.

Boundary	α	Consequences
soft tissue/soft tissue	0.01 (1%)	very small echoes but detectable with suitable amplification
bone/soft tissue	0.4 (40%)	strong echoes but transmission and hence imaging beyond bone can be difficult
air/soft tissue	0.999 (99.9%)	coupling medium needed to transmit ultrasound into body. Imaging beyond air spaces, e.g. lungs, impossible

Coupling medium

A coupling medium is essential between the ultrasound transducer and the body surface to prevent the excessive reflections which occur at any air/soft tissue boundary (see table 1.2). Early techniques involved immersing the patient and transducer probe in a water bath, but the modern method is to smear a film of oil or gel onto the patient's skin before application of the probe. This previents air being trapped between probe and skin and ensures the efficient transmission of ultrasound into the body (see figure 1.10).

ULTRASONIC SCANNING

The sonar principle

Sonar, an acronym for **SO**und **NA**vigation and **R**anging, was developed during World War I for submarine detection. It relies on the reflection of ultrasound pulses (figure 1.6(a)).

A short pulse of ultrasound is directed towards the object of interest, which then reflects it back as an echo. The total time t between transmission of pulse and reception of echo is measured, often using a **cathode ray oscilloscope (CRO)**. If the velocity c of ultrasound in the medium is also known, the depth d of the structure can be found using

$$\textbf{distance = velocity} \times \textbf{time} \qquad \textbf{(1.3)}$$

$$d = \frac{ct}{2}$$

The factor of 2 is necessary since the pulse has to travel 'there and back'.

The application of this range-finding technique to medical imaging is clear. An ultrasound beam is directed into the body. The reflections, or echoes, from different body structures are then detected and analysed, yielding information about their locations. For example, if the time delay between the reception of echo pulses 1 and 2 (figure 1.6(b)) is t, then the diameter of the baby's head can be found using the above formula.

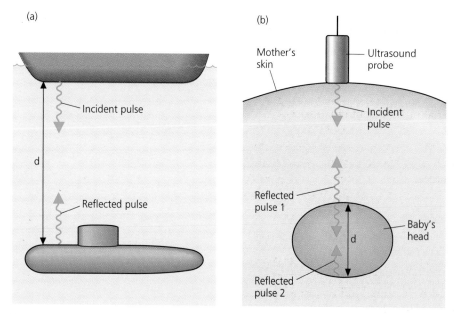

Figure 1.6 Echo location: **(a)** conventional sonar; **(b)** medical imaging.

Range-finding – Worked example

During an eye investigation, the time delay for an echo to return from a structure is 10.5 µs. If the average velocity of ultrasound in the eye is $1510\,\mathrm{m\,s^{-1}}$, calculate the depth of the structure.

The depth d is found using equation 1.3:

$$d = \frac{ct}{2}$$

$$\therefore \quad d = \frac{1510\,\mathrm{m\,s^{-1}} \times 10.5 \times 10^{-6}\,\mathrm{s}}{2}$$

$$= 7.93 \times 10^{-3}\,\mathrm{m}$$

$$= 7.93\,\mathrm{mm}$$

REFLECTION

- **Ultrasound imaging** relies on the reflection of ultrasound at body interfaces.
- The strength of the echo depends on the **intensity reflection coefficient**, α, across the boundary.

$$\alpha = \frac{(Z_2 - Z_1)^2}{(Z_2 + Z_1)^2}$$

Large differences in Z lead to large values of α and strong echoes.

- Any boundary with air results in almost 100% reflection (**coupling medium** needed to introduce ultrasound into the body).
- The **sonar principle** is used to estimate the depth of a structure, using

$$d = \frac{ct}{2}.$$

THE A-SCAN

The **A-** (or Amplitude) **scan** is essentially a *range-measuring* system. It operates by recording the time taken, t, for an ultrasonic pulse to travel to an interface in the body and be reflected back. The time-measuring instrument is the CRO, which must therefore be synchronised with the transmitter/receiver system (figure 1.7).

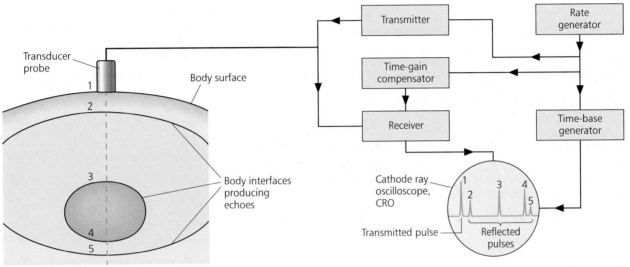

Figure 1.7 A block diagram of the A-scan system.

The rate generator

At regular intervals, this *simultaneously* activates (a) the transmitter; (b) the time-base generator; (c) the time-gain compensator.

- The **transmitter** stimulates the piezoelectric transducer to emit a short (few microseconds) sharp pulse of ultrasound into the body.
- The **time-base generator** supplies a voltage across the X-plates (horizontal deflection) of the CRO so that the spot starts moving steadily across the screen.
- The **time-gain compensator** controls the exact amplification (or gain) of the returning signal, as described below.

Receiver

A voltage is generated in the transducer probe whenever an ultrasound pulse arrives there. This occurs both when the initial pulse is sent out, and when reflected pulses return from the patient. These voltages are amplified at the receiver and applied to the Y-plates of the CRO, causing a vertical deflection of the moving spot. A vertical line thus appears on the screen each time an echo returns to the probe. The positions of these lines on the screen (e.g. 1, 2, 3, 4, 5,) correspond to the positions of the associated reflecting surfaces in the body (i.e. 1 (body surface), 2, 3, 4, 5).

Time-gain compensator

Due to attenuation of the ultrasound pulses in the body, echoes from deeper interfaces tend to be very weak. These weak signals might contain valuable information. To ensure that they are not lost, they are amplified more than those originating close to the probe using the time-gain compensator. This increases the gain of the receiver with time at an appropriate rate, a technique known as **time-gain compensation**, TGC.

Cathode ray oscilloscope

One complete movement of the spot across the screen corresponds to the transmission of one pulse and the receipt of a number of echoes. If this entire process is repeated very rapidly a continuous trace is seen on the screen. Such a trace is shown in figure 1.8, a typical A-scan from a fetal head. The large peaks A and B correspond to echoes from the two sides of the skull, whilst the smaller peak C is due to an echo from what is known as the mid-line of the brain.

Using the CRO's calibrated time base (often in μs cm⁻¹) estimates of time intervals between echoes may be made. For example, the time t elapsing between peaks A and B on the screen can be recorded. This corresponds to the time taken for an ultrasound pulse to travel from the near side of the baby's skull to the far side, *and back again*. Then, knowing the velocity c of the pulse in the tissue (1500 m s⁻¹) the diameter of the baby's head may be evaluated, using equation 1.3:

$$d = \frac{ct}{2}$$

This diameter is a good indication of the age of the developing baby, and can be used to predict a delivery date. Such A-scan measurements have been widely used in the routine screening of pregnant women.

Although the CRO is essentially a *time*-measurer here, it may be directly calibrated to give *distances* between reflecting interfaces in the body, by assuming an average value for c.

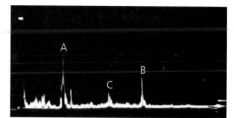

Figure 1.8 A-scan of a fetal head (about 18 weeks from conception).

The A-scan – Worked example

During an A-scan it is required to present echoes from structures as far as the rear wall of the heart, which can be up to 20 cm from the chest wall. If the velocity of ultrasound in the body is 1500 m s⁻¹, select a suitable time base in μs cm⁻¹ on the monitoring CRO such that the entire display of echoes spans about 10 cm.

Rearranging equation 1.3, $d = \frac{ct}{2}$, we can first find the time delay t between echoes from the chest surface and the far wall of the heart:

$$\begin{aligned}
t &= \frac{2d}{c} \\
&= \frac{2 \times 0.2 \text{ m}}{1500 \text{ m s}^{-1}} \\
&= 2.67 \times 10^{-4} \text{ s} \\
&= 267 \text{ μs}
\end{aligned}$$

If this time range is to be displayed in 10 cm of the CRO scale, each centimetre must accommodate 26.7 μs.

Hence, a suitable time-base calibration would be 30 μs cm⁻¹.

THE A-SCAN

- The **A-scan** is a **range finder**, estimating depths of, or distances between, body structures. Distances are calculated using
$$d = \frac{ct}{2}$$
Time is measured using a CRO.
- **Short ultrasonic pulses** are transmitted into the body and their returning echo pulses are applied to the **Y-plates** of a CRO.
- **Reflecting surfaces** in the body are presented on the CRO as vertical peaks:
the **amplitude** of a peak represents the strength of the echo,
the **position** of the peak is determined by the depth of the reflecting surface and the time base used on the CRO.
- The major **components** of the system are the rate generator, transmitter, time-base generator, receiver, time-gain compensator and CRO.
- It is used to measure the **diameter of the fetal head**, and distances within the eye.

THE B-SCAN

In the **B-** (or Brightness) **scan**, the echo signals are not applied to the Y-plates of the CRO but instead are used to control the *brightness* of the spot on the screen. Hence, the static B-scan displays the range of reflecting surfaces using spots whose brightness give a measure of echo amplitude. The time base is applied to the Y-plates. This produces a static B-scan as shown in figure 1.9.

On its own the static B-scan is not very useful. However, it forms the basis of several invaluable scanning systems and is now by far the most commonly used mode.

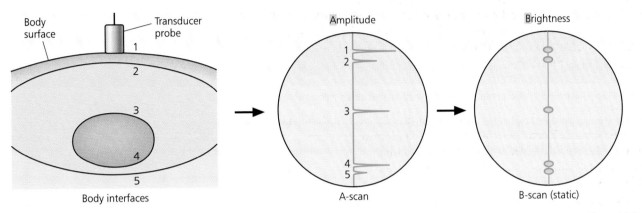

Figure 1.9 Static B-scan.

The simple sector scan

In the sector scan, the probe is 'rocked' on the patient, so that the ultrasound beam sweeps through a fan-shaped sector of interest, rather like the sweeping action of a windscreen wiper on a car (figure 1.10). A series of static B-scans, like CD, is thus obtained, with the time base moving around with the direction CD of the scan. During a 'sweep', data for each static scan is stored, so that gradually a two-dimensional image of a section or wedge through the patient is reconstructed.

Such a *cross-sectional* picture in the plane of the scan is sometimes called a **tomograph** (after the Greek *tomos*, meaning 'a section') and the associated study is termed tomography.

Figure 1.10 A simple sector B-scan.

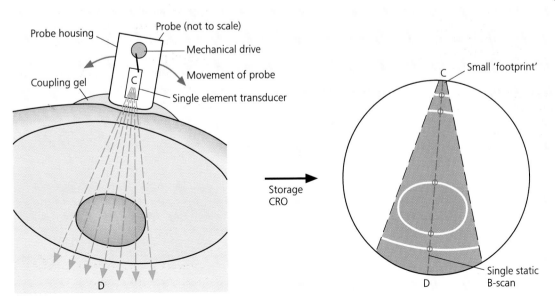

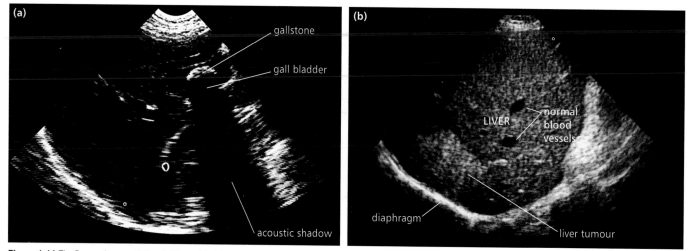

Figure 1.11 The B-scan is essentially a 'white on black' image: strong echoes produce white areas, while echo-free regions are black. For example, fluid-filled structures, like the gall bladder (**a**), produce large echoes from their walls, which consequently appear white, but no echoes from the fluid contained within them, which thus looks black. In this example, the strong echo-producing stone appears white, and in fact creates an 'acoustic shadow' beyond it (see page 18). In (**b**), the contrast between the light appearance of the diaphragm and liver tumour (strong echoes), the grey liver tissue (some echoes), and the black cross-sections of normal blood vessels (no echoes), is clear.

The simple sector scan suffers from the need to have extremely skilled and experienced operators in order to get clear images. Furthermore, it provides a relatively poor quality focusing, so it has now largely disappeared from routine hospital work. However, its advantage of only requiring a small entry 'window' or 'footprint' makes it suitable still for particular applications, like imaging the infant brain through the fontanel (a space between component bones of the skull) (see figure 1.3).

Real-time scans

Most hospital ultrasound scanning now uses **real-time imaging**, enabling doctors to observe events 'live', as they are happening. This relies on the use of **multiple-element transducers**, in which arrays of often hundreds of piezoelectric transducers are arranged in the probe head.

Sophisticated electronic equipment causes one or a group of transducers to 'fire' ultrasound pulses into the body and receive the various echoes sequentially, (figure 1.12). Within a fraction of a second all the information is received, analysed and displayed on a monitor, giving effectively a 'real-time' image of body structures. Even moving organs like the heart are visualised approximately as they are moving.

Much of the recent improvement in image quality is due to advances in transducer array construction and electronic processing. Further details about these arrays can be found on the Web page.

Figure 1.12 Real-time scanning using a multiple-element transducer.

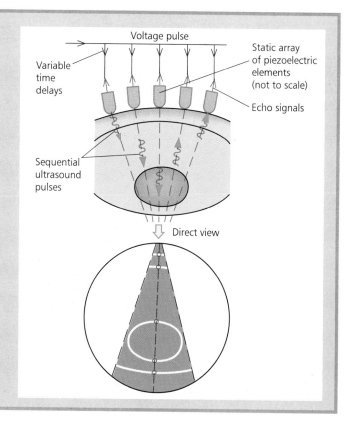

M-scan

The **M-** (or Motion) **scan** allows *moving* structures, such as heart valves, to be monitored. The static B-scan is modified by applying a low-velocity time-base generator across, for example, the X-plates of the CRO. During the sweep time (3 s) the B-scan is moved horizontally at a constant low velocity. Thus, if any of the examined reflecting interfaces moves during this time, their movement creates vertical deflections in the horizontal line pattern displayed. Figure 1.13 illustrates five reflecting surfaces only one of which (4) is moving. For example, this could be the mitral valve in the heart.

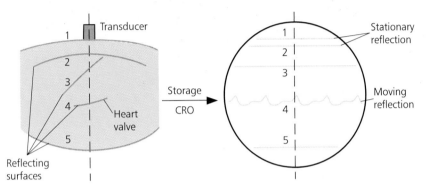

Figure 1.13 The M-scan.

Even with the advent of real-time scanning, the M-scan is still sometimes preferred for the investigation of the exact movement of adult heart valves and fetal hearts, since greater detail of movement can be observed.

THE B-SCAN

- Returning echo pulses are fed to the **brightness** control on the CRO giving a **static B-scan**: the **brightness** of the spot represents the echo strength, the **position** of the spot is determined by the position of the reflecting surface, and the time base used on the CRO.
- Sector scanning provides an image of a slice through the body (a **tomograph**).
- Used to **image** babies in their mothers' wombs and abdominal structures.

Digital imaging

Most echo patterns are now transformed into digital signals, so that they can easily be stored in a computer memory and later reconstructed and displayed on a monitor.

After a single ultrasound pulse has been sent into the body, a number of echoes return from various body interfaces. These stimulate the transducer to produce a string of **voltage pulses** (proportional to echo intensity) at specific **times** (proportional to depth of reflector in the body). This collection of voltage/time values is recorded in digital form, and represents the information contained along a single line in the image (like the information displayed in a static B-scan) (see figure 1.9).

Subsequent ultrasound pulses then generate further sets of 'line data', all of which are stored in the computer memory. The final image is then reconstructed, line by line, on the video display, either immediately (in 'real time') or later as required.

A frame freeze option enables a single frame to be examined or a structure measured using the on-screen callipers.

With increased computer speeds and memories, it is also possible to produce and store sequential scans of a large number of slightly displaced sections through the body. A 3-D representation of the body structure can then be reconstructed (figure 1.14).

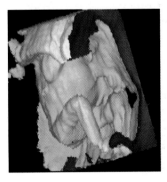

Figure 1.14 A 3-D scan of a 20-week fetus, showing the trunk and limbs.

IMAGE CLARITY

Resolution

Resolution describes the *fineness of detail* observable in an image: good resolution implies that very small structures can be distinguished.

When considering an ultrasound image, there are two types of resolution: axial and lateral (figure 1.15). **Axial** (or depth) **resolution** (along the axis of the beam) describes the ability of the beam to detect, as separate, two objects at different distances, both directly in the path of the beam. It depends on pulse duration: the shorter the pulse, the better the axial resolution.

Heavy damping in the transducer leads to short pulse durations of less than 1 μs. This results in axial resolutions of between 0.1 and 1 mm. If two surfaces are closer together than this, they will be 'seen' as a single surface.

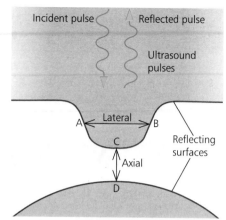

Figure 1.15 Axial and lateral resolution.

Axial resolution – Worked example

For the reception of two distinct echoes from C and D in figure 1.15, the separation

$$\mathbf{CD} > \frac{1}{2} \times \textbf{pulse length}$$

(Otherwise, the reflections from C and D will be part of the same wave pulse, and will not be separable.)

A typical pulse may contain 3 complete waves. If a source of 12 MHz is used, and the pulse velocity is 1500 m s⁻¹, estimate the value of CD.

The time to emit 1 wave is $\dfrac{1}{12 \times 10^6\,\text{s}^{-1}}$. Thus a typical pulse containing 3 waves will take $\dfrac{3}{12 \times 10^6\,\text{s}^{-1}}$.

$$\textbf{Pulse length = pulse velocity} \times \textbf{pulse duration}$$

$$= 1500\,\text{m s}^{-1} \times \frac{3}{12 \times 10^6\,\text{s}^{-1}} = 375 \times 10^{-6}\,\text{m}$$

$$\therefore \textbf{CD} > \frac{1}{2} \times 375 \times 10^{-6}\,\text{m} = 0.188\,\textbf{mm}$$

i.e. the axial resolution would be quoted as approximately 0.2 mm.

Since there is usually the same number of cycles in a 'pulse', regardless of frequency, short wavelengths (and therefore high frequencies) give shorter pulse lengths and better axial resolution.

Lateral resolution describes detail distinguishable at right angles to the beam. For example, will the lump AB in the top reflecting surface of figure 1.15 be detectable?

Firstly, lateral resolution depends on beam width: narrow beams give good resolution. (This can further be improved using the sophisticated focusing capabilities of phased arrays (see Web page).) Secondly, high-frequency beams produce better lateral resolution due to a reduction in diffraction blur, (see box).

However, as we have already seen (page 7), high-frequency beams suffer the greatest absorption. Hence, a compromise is necessary between resolution and penetration, restricting the practical frequency range as shown in table 1.3. Different probes are used for different frequency ranges – the most common range being between 3 and 10 MHz.

Table 1.3 Ultrasound frequency ranges.

Frequency (MHz)	Typical penetration depth (cm)	Resolution (mm)	Structures investigated
3–5	10–20	1.0	*deep:* heart, uterus, liver
4–10	5	0.2	*quite superficial:* thyroid, carotid artery, breast
10–15	1	0.1	*very superficial:* eye
50 (highly specialised)	few mm	0.05	skin or surgical investigations (blood vessel walls, cartilage)

Diffraction effects

Diffraction describes the *spreading of waves* as they pass obstacles or go through apertures. It becomes significant when the size of the obstacle is so small that it approaches the wavelength of the waves (or the wavelength of the waves is so large that it approaches the size of the obstacle!).

Any such spread in the ultrasound beam results in blurring or reduction in resolution (figure 1.16). Thus, to minimise diffraction blur, the wavelength should be chosen so that it is less than the 'obstacle' size. For example, if an ultrasound beam is to resolve objects of about 1 mm across, the wavelength λ should be chosen such that:

$$\lambda \leq 1\,mm$$
$$\therefore \quad \frac{c}{f} \leq 10^{-3}\,m \qquad \text{and } c = 1500\,m\,s^{-1}$$
$$\therefore \quad f \geq \frac{1500\,m\,s^{-1}}{10^{-3}\,m}$$
$$\therefore \quad f \geq 1.5 \times 10^{6}\,Hz$$
$$f \geq 1.5\,MHz$$

Thus, a frequency exceeding 1.5 MHz should be selected. Alternatively, to achieve a lateral resolution of 0.1 mm, a 15 MHz beam would have to be employed.

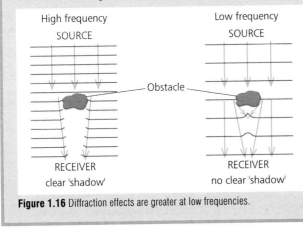

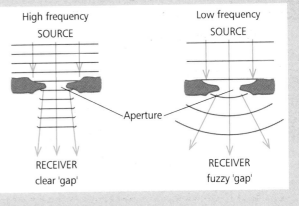

Figure 1.16 Diffraction effects are greater at low frequencies.

Grey-scale imaging

The range of echo intensities coming from the tissues is extremely large, typically 90 dB (i.e. the intensity of the strongest signal is 10^{9} times that of the weakest). Half of this range is due to absorption and may be compensated for using the time-gain compensator. However, the remainder is due to the nature of the reflecting surfaces encountered, particularly the differences in acoustic impedance across the interfaces.

Before the introduction of the grey-scale system of imaging in 1974, this resulted in strong echoes all being displayed at similarly high intensities whilst valuable small echoes failed to register at all. Now, using **selective amplification**, it is possible to create a suitable enhancement of the particular level of echo (or shade of grey) of interest. For example, strong echoes, possibly half the total range, may be displayed as white, whilst the remaining echoes are spread across a suitable grey scale to highlight subtle textural differences in soft tissue, that would previously have been lost.

Artefacts

An artefact is an unwanted signal.

Multiple reflection artefacts

When a reflected pulse arrives back at the transducer most of the energy is transmitted to the receiver for subsequent registration on the display. However, some of the energy pulse is reflected back into the body for another 'round trip'. When it next appears back at the transducer an artefact is displayed on the screen. Such multiple reflection artefacts are usually recognised by the regularity of their spacings.

Movement artefacts

Except when internal movement is being studied, any movement of the patient can blur the scan. Such movements include the involuntary movements of vital organs, shifting of the fetus in the womb, and so on.

Acoustic shadowing

This refers to the reduced amplitude of echoes from the region behind strongly reflecting structures, like gallstones (see figure 1.11(a)).

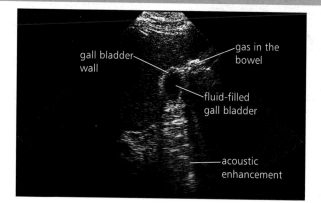

Figure 1.17 The gall bladder, being fluid-filled, is echo free, giving rise to an artificially high echo intensity from the region beyond it, (acoustic enhancement). Note also the bright appearance of the gas pockets in the bowel, since gas/soft tissue interfaces are strong reflectors.

Acoustic enhancement

Conversely, there is an increase in echo amplitude behind weakly absorbing structures, like the gall bladder (figure 1.17).

APPLICATIONS OF PULSE-ECHO IMAGING

Although the A-scan is occasionally used for measuring axial distances in the eye, it is largely obsolete. It is nevertheless useful to understand its mode of operation, since its range-finding technique still forms the basis of the other more sophisticated scanning systems.

Obstetrics

Being harmless to mother and baby, ultrasound finds many applications in obstetrics.

Routine monitoring of fetal development (figure 1.18) is most easily carried out by B-scan observation of the fetus (figure 1.19), followed by a measurement of the baby's head size, which provides an estimate of the length of gestation. A delivery date can be predicted, and any problems such as heart, brain or spine abnormalities, can be diagnosed.

Ultrasound is successfully used to locate the placenta, the organ on the wall of the womb through which the fetus is nourished. If the placenta is across the exit from the womb, a normal delivery is difficult and a Caesarian section is recommended. Multiple pregnancy, ectopic pregnancy (growth of the fetus outside the womb) and breech presentations (feet first), are amongst other conditions easily diagnosed.

IMAGE CLARITY

- **Resolution** describes the **fineness of detail** observable in the image:
  axial (depth information): better with **shorter pulses.**
  lateral (side-to-side information): better with **narrow beams** and **higher frequencies.**
- Higher frequencies give better resolution but reduced penetration.
- **Grey-scale** imaging is used to enhance subtle soft-tissue differences.
- Imaging beyond **bone** (too much absorption) and **air** (too much reflection), is difficult.
- **Artefacts** (unwanted signals) might confuse the final image.

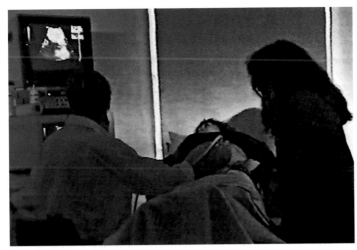

Figure 1.18 Routine pre-natal scan.

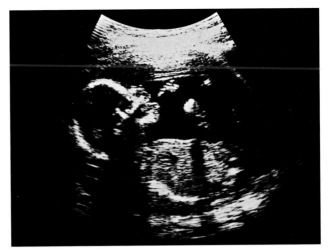

Figure 1.19 An ultrasound scan of an unborn baby, who has already learnt about thumb-sucking.

Abdominal investigations

Due to its excellent soft-tissue discrimination, ultrasound is used extensively in abdominal studies. The liver, kidneys and pancreas are frequently imaged, leading to the diagnosis, for example, of tumours, cysts and stones (see figures 1.11 and 1.17).

Ultrasound cardiography (UCG)

The front of the heart is largely covered by the lungs and pleura, which effectively 'block' ultrasound due to the presence of air. However, there is a small 'window' in the chest wall through which the heart may be investigated using ultrasound. Considerable experience is necessary to register and interpret a clear scan from the heart, and it is important to relax the subject first, since fast heart rates are less likely to produce a successful ultrasound cardiogram (UCG).

DOPPLER SYSTEMS

All of the systems considered so far have used **pulse–echo techniques**, relying on the *range-finding* capability of short, sharp pulses. In contrast, Doppler systems monitor the *velocities* of moving structures by detecting frequency changes in the reflected signals. They can therefore employ either continuous or pulsed waves.

Doppler scans are often used in conjunction with standard pulse-echo imaging, the instruments available ranging from simple 'pocket-size' versions, giving audio outputs only, to sophisticated colour-flow machines costing hundreds of thousands of pounds (figure 1.20).

The Doppler effect

The Doppler effect is the *apparent change in frequency* registered by an observer when there is a relative motion between the source and observer. This phenomenon, first described by the Austrian Christian Doppler in 1842, has many modern examples, perhaps the most common being the apparent rise and then fall in pitch (frequency) of a siren as it approaches then recedes from an observer. The effect relies on an understanding of the wavefronts emitted (figure 1.21).

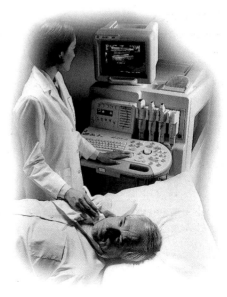

Figure 1.20 A colour Doppler machine.

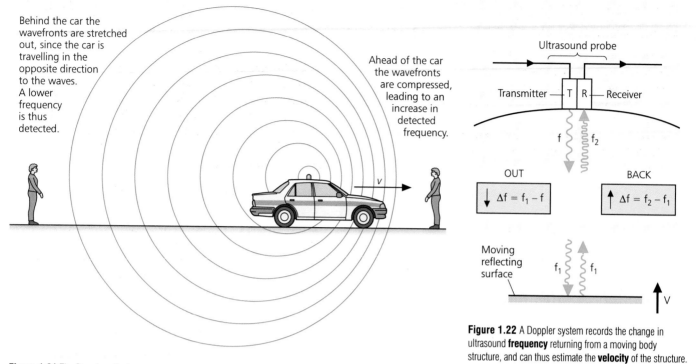

Behind the car the wavefronts are stretched out, since the car is travelling in the opposite direction to the waves. A lower frequency is thus detected.

Ahead of the car the wavefronts are compressed, leading to an increase in detected frequency.

Figure 1.21 The Doppler effect.

Ultrasound probe

Transmitter — T R — Receiver

f f_2

OUT   BACK

$\downarrow \Delta f = f_1 - f$ $\uparrow \Delta f = f_2 - f_1$

Moving reflecting surface f_1 f_1

V

Figure 1.22 A Doppler system records the change in ultrasound **frequency** returning from a moving body structure, and can thus estimate the **velocity** of the structure.

The Doppler shift

The apparent change in frequency Δf experienced as a result of the Doppler effect is known as the **Doppler shift**. Its value increases as the *relative* velocity v between the source and the observer increases.

If v is very much smaller than the velocity c of the waves themselves, it can be shown that the Doppler shift is given by

$$\Delta f = \frac{fv}{c} \quad (v<<c)$$

where f is the *actual* frequency of the source.

When source and observer approach each other (i.e. the detected frequency increases) Δf is positive, and when they move apart Δf is negative.

Such a Doppler shift in frequency occurs when ultrasound waves are reflected from *moving* body surfaces (figure 1.22). A wave, of frequency f, is transmitted into the body and reflected from the surface moving towards the transmitter with a velocity v. The waves not only suffer a Doppler shift on their outward journey, but also on their return journey, leading to a **double Doppler shift** in total of

$$\Delta f = \frac{2fv}{c} \quad (1.4)$$

If Δf is measured, and f and c are known, v can be found. This is the principle of the Doppler systems used in medicine to record the velocity of moving body structures.

Doppler shift – Worked example

Ultrasound of frequency 5.0 MHz is reflected from a structure in the heart and found to be Doppler shifted by 300 Hz. If the speed of ultrasound in the body is 1.5 km s^{-1}, calculate the speed of the moving structure.

Using equation 1.4:
$$\Delta f = \frac{2fv}{c}$$
$$v = \frac{c\Delta f}{2f}$$
$$= \frac{1500 \text{ m s}^{-1} \times 300 \text{ s}^{-1}}{2 \times 5 \times 10^6 \text{ s}^{-1}}$$
$$= 0.45 \text{ m s}^{-1}$$

The structure is therefore moving either towards, or away from, the probe with a velocity of 0.45 m s^{-1}.

Doppler equations

Moving source, stationary observer

Consider a source of sound of frequency f in a medium in which the wave velocity is c. In 1 s, f waves are emitted and occupy a distance c (figure 1.23(a)). If the source now moves towards a stationary observer with a velocity v, the f waves emitted in 1 s only occupy a distance $(c-v)$ (figure 1.23(b)).

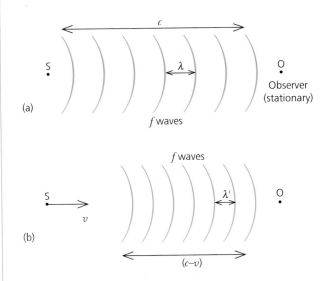

(a)

(b)

Figure 1.23 Wavefront representations: (**a**) stationary source; (**b**) moving source.

As far as the observer is concerned the initial wavelength of the sound when the source is stationary is given by:

$$\lambda = \frac{c}{f}$$

The apparent wavelength, when the source is moving, is given by:

$$\lambda' = \frac{c - v}{f}$$

Hence, the observer registers an apparent frequency:

$$f' = \frac{c}{\lambda'} = \frac{cf}{c - v}$$

which is higher than the true frequency f.

Stationary source, moving observer

Consider now an observer moving at a velocity v towards a stationary source. The f waves emitted by the source in 1 s still occupy a distance c, and their apparent wavelength to the observer is still $\lambda = c/f$. However, the velocity of the waves relative to the observer is now $c+v$, so that the apparent frequency becomes:

$$f'' = \frac{c + v}{\lambda} = \frac{(c + v)f}{c}$$

In the case of a reflection from a moving surface (figure 1.22) we have a combination of these two situations. For the outward journey, the source (transmitter) is stationary and the observer (reflecting surface) is moving

$$f' = \frac{cf}{c - v} \qquad \textbf{(1.5)}$$

On the return journey the source (reflecting surface) is moving and the observer (receiver) is stationary.

$$f'' = \frac{(c + v)f'}{c} \qquad \textbf{(1.6)}$$

Combining the two equations (1.5) and (1.6) gives

$$f'' = \frac{(c + v)}{c} \frac{cf}{(c - v)} = \frac{(c + v)f}{(c - v)}$$

Hence, there is a total Doppler shift of

$$\Delta f = f'' - f = \frac{(c + v)f}{(c - v)} - f$$

$$= \frac{(c + v)f - (c - v)f}{(c - v)} = \frac{2vf}{(c - v)}$$

If $v \ll c$ (as is always the case with moving body structures)

$$\Delta f = \frac{2vf}{c} \qquad \textbf{(1.4)}$$

This is the 'double' Doppler shift referred to in the text.

Continuous wave Doppler system

A simple system for measuring the velocity of body structures is shown in figure 1.24.

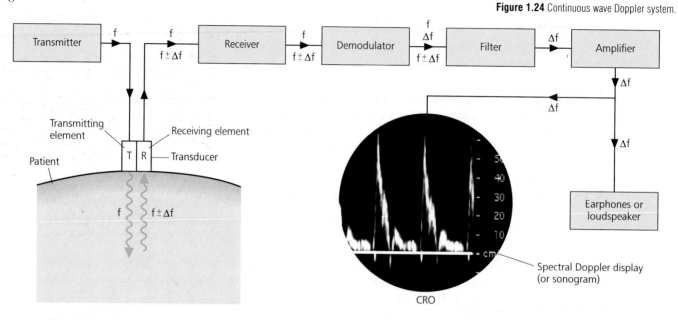

Figure 1.24 Continuous wave Doppler system.

The **transmitter** provides a continuous voltage output of constant amplitude and frequency, the latter generally being about 2–5 MHz.

The **transducer** contains separate transmitting and receiving piezoelectric crystals. This is necessary when using continuous waves, to avoid the inevitable confusion arising if a single crystal tries to emit and receive signals simultaneously!

The **receiver** outputs signals containing

- the same frequency f as the transmitter (due to stationary reflectors)
- the Doppler-shifted frequency (due to the moving reflector), $f \pm \Delta f$.

The **demodulator** mixes the output frequencies to generate Δf separately.
The **filter** removes any frequencies other than Δf.
The **amplifier** further amplifies the remaining signal.

The **recorder-analyser** may simply be the ear, using headphones or a loudspeaker since typical Doppler shifts lie within the audible range. Certain Doppler shifts have a characteristic sound (e.g. the fetal heart Doppler shifts sound like galloping horses; the placenta like wind rushing through trees) and the experienced ear can recognise any abnormalities.

On the other hand, the Doppler shifts (Δf) can be converted directly into velocity (v) using equation 1.4:

$$\Delta f = \frac{2fv}{c}$$

With the help of fast electronic analysis and CRO display, the fluctuation of v with time t can be displayed directly in the form of a graph or **sonogram**, also known as a **spectral Doppler display** (figure 1.24). Positive values of Δf, (v), indicate reflectors moving towards the probe, whilst negative values show reflectors moving away from the probe.

This is a significant improvement on the early Doppler flowmeters that could only record the Doppler shift Δf without even differentiating between flow towards and away from the transducer!

Separation of Δf: beats

Beats describes the periodic rise and fall in intensity of a *resultant* wave, formed by the addition of two component waves of similar, but not identical, frequency. The **beat frequency** is the number of intense signals registered per second and is found to be equal to the difference between the two component frequencies.

When the demodulator adds the two close frequencies, f and $f \pm \Delta f$, beats are formed of frequency Δf. By analysing the *amplitude* of the resultant wave, Δf (which is the Doppler shift too) can be identified.

Blood flow measurement

The Doppler shift technique may be used to estimate the velocity of blood flow in veins and arteries. Since these are generally superficial, attenuation is consequently less important than with deeper structures, and higher ultrasound frequencies in the range 5–15 MHz, are used, giving better resolution. Even at 15 MHz (wavelength 0.1 mm) resolution is no better than 0.1 mm. Since individual red blood cells have diameters of about 6 μm, only the scatter from clumps of cells can be identified.

The region of interest is first imaged using a conventional pulsed wave B-scan. A particular vein or artery is identified and an on-screen cursor is aligned with the direction of flow (figure 1.25(a)). The angle θ between the ultrasound beam and the blood flow is automatically computed (figure 1.25(b)).

Using either a continuous or pulsed wave Doppler system, the ultrasound is directed towards the sample indicated by the cursor. Since the component of the blood flow in the direction of the beam is $v\cos\theta$, the Doppler shift in frequency is given, using equation 1.4, by

$$\Delta f = \frac{(2fv\cos\theta)}{c} \qquad (1.7)$$

The velocity of the blood is thus computed and its variation with time shown on a spectral Doppler display (figure 1.26) (see box).

The main advantage of the system is that surgical penetration of the vessel is unnecessary. Continuous recordings can be made with no risk or discomfort to the patient and can lead for example to flow volume estimates if the vessel diameter is known.

In practice, not all of the blood moves with the same velocity, since frictional resistance reduces it to lower values nearer the vessel walls. Also, the flow is not always parallel to the blood vessel axis, and hence $v\cos\theta$ will not be an accurate representation of blood velocity towards the probe. Hence, a range of velocities will be recorded at each time instant on the display, as shown in figure 1.26.

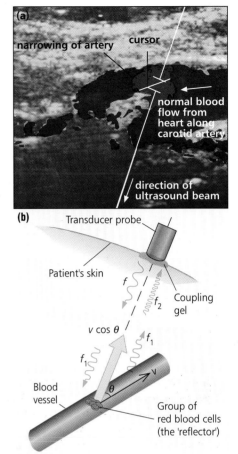

Figure 1.25 (a) B-scan of the carotid artery in the neck, with colour Doppler overlay. Where the artery divides, there is some narrowing, leading to unwanted reverse blood flow towards the transducer, (indicated in red). **(b)** Ultrasound reflection from the moving blood.

Doppler blood flow measurement – Worked example

Blood is flowing through a vessel at an average rate of $1\,\text{m s}^{-1}$. Using an ultrasound beam of frequency 5 MHz, find the Doppler shift registered if the vessel is inclined at $60°$ to the beam, and the velocity of the waves in the body is $1.5\,\text{km s}^{-1}$.

The Doppler shift is given by equation 1.7:

$$\Delta f = \frac{2fv\cos\theta}{c}$$
$$= \frac{2 \times 5 \times 10^6\,\text{s}^{-1} \times 1\,\text{m s}^{-1} \times \cos 60}{1500\,\text{m s}^{-1}}$$
$$= 3.3 \times 10^3\,\text{Hz}$$
$$= 3.3\,\text{kHz}$$

Thus, the Doppler shift recorded is 3.3 kHz, which falls within the audible range.

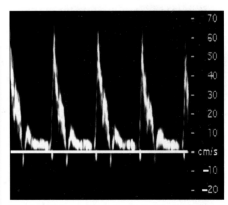

Figure 1.26 Spectral Doppler display. The trace shows the variation in blood velocity with time in the carotid artery at the position of the cursor in figure 1.25 (a). Note that the velocity values are almost entirely positive, (towards the transducer), again indicating the reverse flow at the narrowing.

The spectral Doppler display

Each dot on the spectral Doppler display (or sonogram) in figure 1.26 contains three pieces of information:

- the velocity v of the moving structure (ordinate)
- the time at which the signal was received (abscissa)
- the strength or amplitude of the signal, which is depicted using a grey scale.

For example, if blood flow were being monitored, the 'brightness' of the spectral Doppler display trace at a given point would indicate *how much* blood, moving at the measured velocity, is reflecting the ultrasound back. If all the grey-scale values are summed over a given time interval (e.g. the forward part of the cycle) an estimate of total volume flow rate could be made.

The **flow pattern** can also be investigated by studying the variation in the velocities recorded on the spectral Doppler display. For example, turbulent flow, often a sign of narrowing of the vessel, results in a large *spread* in velocity values.

Pulsed–wave Doppler systems

A disadvantage of using *continuous* waves is that they cannot be used for range-finding and hence for producing images of anatomy.

Most modern Doppler instruments employ short *pulses* of ultrasound rather than continuous waves. By analysis of the reflected Doppler shifted pulses, the following information can be displayed:

- a conventional real-time B-mode image showing basic body structure
- a corresponding 'colour overlay' of mean velocity values at each location (figure 1.25(a))
- a separate spectral Doppler display of a selected sample region (figure 1.26).

To produce the 'colour overlay', velocity values are colour-coded – the red end of the spectrum representing velocities towards the transducer and the blue end of the spectrum representing velocities away from the transducer. Intermediate colours represent the full range of velocities recorded. The technique is known as **colour Doppler** or simply **flow imaging**.

Such blood flow 'mapping' (rather like the familiar map of the physical geography of a region, where different heights are indicated in different colours) is especially useful in heart studies. For example, leaky heart valves result in flow in the 'wrong' direction, and are easily recognised by streaks of the 'wrong' colour (figure 1.27). Holes in the heart are similarly diagnosed.

The spectral Doppler display is also useful for recognising **flow patterns**. A large variation in blood velocity values suggests irregular flow.

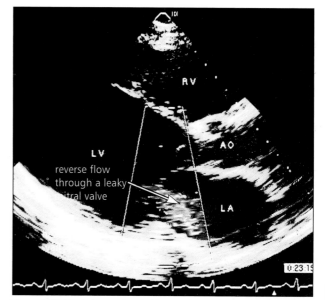

Figure 1.27 A leaky heart valve. At this stage in the heart's pumping action, the mitral valve should be firmly closed. However, the colour Doppler display shows some leakage of blood back into the left atrium (LA).

Key
RV = right ventricle
LV = left ventricle
LA = left atrium
AO = aorta

APPLICATIONS OF DOPPLER IMAGING

Fetal heart monitoring (fetal cardiology)

During both pregnancy and delivery the fetal heart beat can be monitored using the 'ultrasonic stethoscope' and used as an indicator of well-being. Blood flow in the fetus and umbilical cord can also be assessed, although this is less common.

Adult heart studies (cardiology)

The performance of heart valves and general flow patterns can be investigated. Leaky or constricted valves (figure 1.27), blockages and holes in the heart are easily diagnosed by the abnormal flows generated. The motion of the heart wall itself can be investigated using selective filters to remove blood flow signals.

Blood circulation

Narrowing (or 'hardening') of the arteries is due to the deposition on the vessel walls of a fatty substance called plaque. The increased blood velocities, turbulence and reduced volume flow rates arising at such constrictions are identifiable, often using simple hand-held Doppler flowmeters with audible outputs. For example, the greater the blood velocity, the higher the pitch heard and the greater the turbulence, the harsher the sound. More sophisticated outputs however give better detail (see figures 1.25 and 26).

Thrombosis (blockage of the vessel due to clots) is clearly diagnosed since there is no flow at all!

The carotid artery (feeding the brain) is particularly well imaged (see figure 1.25). Because of its superficial location at the side of the neck, high frequencies can be employed, giving excellent resolution.

The blood flow in abdominal structures, like the liver, kidneys and spleen, can also readily be imaged (figure 1.28).

BIOLOGICAL EFFECTS OF ULTRASOUND

When delivered at sufficient intensity, high-frequency ultrasound can induce raised temperatures and considerable mechanical activity in human tissue. The magnitude of the effects depends largely on the intensity, as summarised in table 1.4.

Table 1.4 Biological effects of ultrasound.

Procedure	Typical Intensity (Wm^{-2})	Beam type	Exposure time	Effect (ΔT = increase in tissue temperature)
diagnosis	10–30	Doppler: continuous	several minutes	negligible
	10–10^4	pulsed	several minutes	$\Delta T \leq 1\,°C$ generally Caution at high intensities
physiotherapy	10^4	continuous	10–30 min	gentle ($\Delta T \sim 5\,°C$) 'deep heat' (hyperthermia)
surgery	10^6	focused multiple beams	0.1–10 s	$\Delta T \sim 30 \rightarrow 50\,°C$ Tissue damage or total destruction

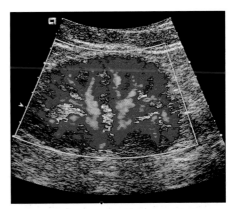

Figure 1.28 Doppler investigation of the kidney: abnormal blood flow patterns are readily recognised.

DOPPLER SYSTEMS

- The **Doppler effect** is the apparent change in frequency when there is relative motion between transmitter and receiver.
- Doppler systems measure the **Doppler shift,** Δf, in ultrasound frequency in the echoes from moving reflectors in the body.
- Δf gives a value for the velocity of the moving reflector,

$$\Delta f = \frac{2fv}{c} \quad \text{or} \quad \frac{2fv\cos\theta}{c}$$

  and is positive (reflector moving towards the transducer), or negative (moving away from it).
- Δf is in the **audible** frequency range, monitored by **ear**, (using headphones), or a **spectral Doppler display** (on a CRO).
- A **continuous wave Doppler system** consists of the transmitter, transducer, receiver, demodulator, filter, amplifier and recorder (earphones, loudspeaker or monitor).
- Used to monitor the **adult** and **fetal hearts**, and **blood flow** in vessels and abdominal structures.

A **thermal effect** arises essentially because the ultrasound wave imposes increased random vibrations onto the molecules of the medium, thereby increasing its temperature.

Ultrasound, like all sound waves, is a pressure wave, exhibiting regions of compression and rarefaction. **Mechanical effects** are observed in tissue when the magnitude of these pressure variations is sufficiently high. An effect called **cavitation** is thought to be partly responsible, whereby gas bubbles form, grow and then collapse violently during, respectively, the rarefaction and compression stages of the pressure wave cycle. Such intense energetic exchanges can lead to both physical damage and chemical change. Very high tissue temperature can result; blood vessel damage and bleeding can occur; DNA molecules can be broken and body metabolism locally disrupted.

Whilst ultrasound is a valuable therapeutic tool, care must be taken delivering high intensity beams to bone (high absorption coefficient), the eye and reproductive organs. Extra precautions are necessary in obstetrics, to prevent the vulnerable fetus receiving the higher power pulsed waves delivered by some diagnostic machines.

Ultrasound therapy

The gentle 'deep-heating' effect of ultrasound accelerates tissue metabolism and is believed to be beneficial in the treatment of arthritic joints, sports injuries and other muscular and joint problems. There is evidence that it speeds up bone repair and wound healing, thereby assisting with such conditions as skin ulcers.

The more intense beams used to destroy tissue involve both thermal and mechanical effects. Kidney and gallstones can be torn apart, and localised areas of unwanted tissue (such as an enlarged portion of the prostate gland) may be destroyed by multiple focused beams.

ADVANTAGES AND DISADVANTAGES OF ULTRASOUND

Advantages
1 Clear examination of **soft tissue**, e.g. obstetrics and abdominal studies.
2 **No** known **harmful effects** of diagnostic ultrasound.
3 **Equipment** is **safe**, easy to handle, can be operated from an ordinary wall socket and can be portable.
4 **Real-time imaging**.
5 More **cost effective** than other imaging modalities.

Disadvantages
1 Cannot penetrate **bone**, so the adult skeletal system and head cannot be imaged.
2 Almost **100% reflection at air interfaces**, necessitating the use of a coupling medium, and making imaging beyond air spaces (e.g. lung) difficult.
3 Scan can take a **long time**, and demands great skill and experience to produce clear results.
4 **Clarity of image** is **poorer** than in many other techniques.

See also page 3 for a full comparison of the imaging modalities.

QUESTIONS

1 Mechanical waves can be either transverse or longitudinal.
   a Of which type are ultrasound waves?
   b Why is this of importance in medical diagnosis?
   c What range of frequencies is commonly used in diagnosis?

2 **a** Explain the following terms:
   i ultrasound
   ii acoustic impedance
   iii intensity reflection coefficient.
   b Why is a coupling medium necessary between a source of ultrasound and the body during ultrasonic investigation of the body?

3 Ultrasound frequencies up to about 300 kHz are used in underwater sonar and animal echolocation studies. Why are these frequencies much lower than those used in medical diagnosis?

4 Acoustic impedance $Z = \rho c$ where ρ is the density of a material and c is the speed of sound in the material. When sound intensity I_i is incident at the boundary between materials of acoustic impedance Z_1 and Z_2 the reflected intensity, I_r is given by

$$\frac{I_r}{I_i} = \left(\frac{Z_2 - Z_1}{Z_2 + Z_1}\right)^2$$

   a Explain how the magnitude of the reflected signal or echo from an ultrasound scan is affected by the change in the acoustic impedance of the material at either side of a reflecting surface or boundary.
   b Use the following data:
   speed of sound in first material = 1500 m s⁻¹...

   speed of sound in first material $= 1500\,\text{m s}^{-1}$
   speed of sound in second material $= 1550\,\text{m s}^{-1}$
   density of first material $= 900\,\text{kg m}^{-3}$
   density of second material $= 1000\,\text{kg m}^{-3}$
   incident intensity, I_i $= 1.0\,\text{W m}^{-2}$
   i Calculate the intensity of the wave reflected at the boundary.
   ii Calculate the intensity of the wave transmitted into the second material.
   (NEAB 1996)

5 The distance between pulses representing ultrasonic reflections from opposite sides of a fetal head was recorded on the screen of a cathode ray oscilloscope as 5.6 cm when the timebase was set to 25 μs cm⁻¹. Calculate the fetal head size assuming the speed of ultrasound in the head is 1.50 km s⁻¹.
   (ULEAC 1990)

6 The diagram (figure 1.30) shows the oscilloscope display of pulse amplitude against time for an ultrasound A-scan through a person's abdomen. Assume that the weaker echoes come from internal organs.
   a Describe the procedures which are used to obtain this type of scan.
   b Explain how the spacing of the pulses is interpreted.

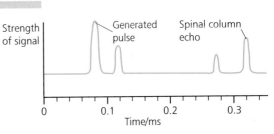

Figure 1.30

   c Give **two** reasons why the amplitude of the reflected pulses varies.
   d If the speed of ultrasound through water and soft tissue is about 1500 m s⁻¹, estimate the distance between the front of the patient's abdomen and the spinal column.
   (NEAB 1996)

7 Explain carefully what information is being plotted on the cathode ray oscilloscope screen during:
   a an A-scan
   b a simple sector B-scan
   c a continuous wave Doppler investigation.

8 **a** Explain the Doppler effect in sound using an illustration showing wave fronts.
   b In diagnostic ultrasound, echo pulses are said to have undergone a 'double Doppler shift'. What is meant by this?
   c Why can continuous ultrasound waves be employed in a medical Doppler system but not in a B-scan system?

9 **a** A 2.2 MHz ultrasound beam travels at a speed of 1.5 km s⁻¹ through soft tissue, and is reflected normally from a moving surface. A Doppler shift of 400 Hz is detected. Calculate the speed of the moving surface.
   b Explain why ultrasound of high frequency (≈ 10 MHz) is used for scanning an eye, but a lower frequency (≈ 3 MHz) is more suitable for abdominal scans.
   (ULEAC 1993)

10 **a** During a blood flow determination, ultrasound of frequency 3 MHz is transmitted at an angle of 30° to the blood vessel. If the velocity of ultrasound is taken to be 1.55 km s⁻¹ and the diameter of the vessel to be 1.2 mm, estimate the blood volume flow rate if a Doppler shift in frequency of 1500 Hz is recorded.
   b Give two reasons why this is an estimate.

11 **a** Explain why ultrasonic wavelengths of 0.3 mm or less must be used if we wish to 'see' detail in soft tissue down to 0.3 mm. Calculate the frequency of this ultrasound and state whether it is a maximum or a minimum for resolving these small details.
   (Speed of ultrasound in soft tissue = 1560 m s⁻¹.)
   b Why is it necessary to limit the power of the ultrasonic source used in medical diagnosis?
   (ULEAC 1992)

Diagnostic X-rays

Whether you have suffered from a broken arm or dental problems, it is hard to imagine twentieth century medicine without 'X-rays' – those familiar shadow pictures formed by passing X-radiation through the body (figure 2.1). Ever since their discovery by Roentgen in 1895, X-rays have played an important role in medicine. Indeed, they provide an example of the fastest transformation of a scientific discovery into a practical technology.

There are now more X-ray examinations undertaken every year in the UK than any other form of medical imaging (figure 2.2). Despite the small radiation risks involved, X-rays form the mainstay of casualty and fracture clinics, provide routine screening for breast and lung cancer, as well as serving more specialist disciplines such as dental and cardiac units.

In the electromagnetic spectrum, X-rays are found towards the high frequency end (figure 2.4). They are produced in an X-ray tube by bombarding a metal target with very energetic electrons. The resulting beam of X-rays is suitably filtered and directed towards the patient. Depending on the body structure encountered, the X-rays will either pass through or be absorbed. Bone stops most X-rays, whilst air stops none. The beam, with its encoded information, emerges from the patient to expose a photographic film. When developed, this yields a 'picture' of internal body structure.

It all sounds very easy! However, X-rays can be hazardous too, as shown by damage sustained by early workers in the field (figure 2.3). In this chapter, we shall be concerned with ways to obtain the clearest possible X-ray images, with minimum risk to the doctor and patient.

The more damaging nature of X-radiation has lead over the years to its therapeutic applications in, for instance, the destruction of body tumours. These aspects are dealt with separately in Chapter 5: Radiotherapy and radiological protection.

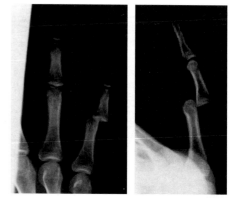

Figure 2.1 X-ray shows two views of a dislocated finger.

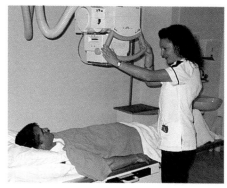

Figure 2.2 A typical X-ray examination.

X-RAYS AND THEIR PRODUCTION

X-radiation is high-frequency electromagnetic radiation of frequency approximately between 10^{17} and 10^{20} Hz (see figure 2.4). It may either be regarded as **waves**, of wavelength λ and frequency f, or as **particles** or **quanta** of energy E. Such packets or quanta of energy are also known as X-ray **photons**.

For **waves**,
$$c = f\lambda$$
where c is wave velocity, f is frequency and λ is wavelength.

For **particles**,
$$E = hf$$
where E is energy and h is Planck's constant ($= 6.63 \times 10^{-34}$ J s).

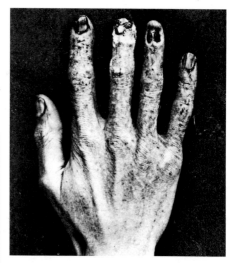

Figure 2.3 Poor radiological protection resulted in severe damage, particulary to doctors' hands.

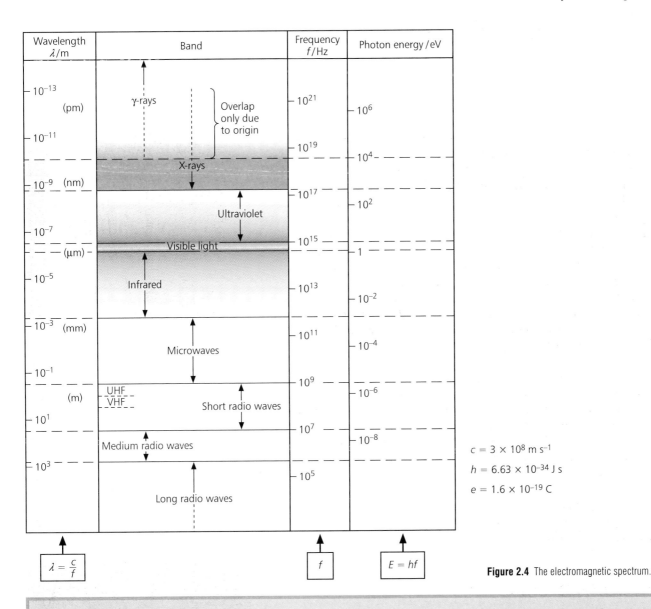

Figure 2.4 The electromagnetic spectrum.

$c = 3 \times 10^8\,\text{m s}^{-1}$

$h = 6.63 \times 10^{-34}\,\text{J s}$

$e = 1.6 \times 10^{-19}\,\text{C}$

X-ray ranges – Worked example

The frequency range of X-rays may be taken as approximately 10^{17}–10^{20} Hz. Calculate the corresponding ranges of their:
a) wavelength
b) photon energy in J
c) photon energy in eV.
($c = 3 \times 10^8\,\text{m s}^{-1}$; $h = 6.63 \times 10^{-34}\,\text{J s}$, $e = 1.6 \times 10^{-19}\,\text{C}$).

a) Wavelength may be found from frequency using $\lambda = c/f$. Thus, the wavelength ranges corresponding to the frequencies of 10^{17} and 10^{20} Hz are

$$\frac{3 \times 10^8\,\text{m s}^{-1}}{10^{17}\,\text{s}^{-1}} \quad \text{to} \quad \frac{3 \times 10^8\,\text{m s}^{-1}}{10^{20}\,\text{s}^{-1}}$$

i.e. 3×10^{-9} m to 3×10^{-12} m

b) Photon energy may be found using $E = hf$. The required range is hence

$6.63 \times 10^{-34}\,\text{J s} \times 10^{17}\,\text{s}^{-1}$ to $6.63 \times 10^{-34}\,\text{J s} \times 10^{20}\,\text{s}^{-1}$

i.e. 6.6×10^{-17} J to 6.6×10^{-14} J

c) To convert J into eV we need to divide by $e = 1.6 \times 10^{-19}\,\text{C}$, since 1 electronvolt $= 1.6 \times 10^{-19}\,\text{J}$ The relevant photon energy range then becomes

$$\frac{6.63 \times 10^{-17}}{1.6 \times 10^{-19}}\ \text{eV} \quad \text{to} \quad \frac{6.63 \times 10^{-14}}{1.6 \times 10^{-19}}\ \text{eV}$$

i.e. about 400 to 400 000 eV or 0.4 to 400 keV

In diagnostic work, a typical X-ray photon energy is around 30 keV.

Production of X-rays in an X-ray tube

Diagnostic X-rays are produced by firing high-speed electrons at a metal target in an **X-ray tube** (figure 2.5).

The electrons are first emitted from a heated filament, by a process called **thermionic emission** (see box). They are then accelerated across the evacuated X-ray tube, under the action of a large voltage across the tube, the filament forming the negative **cathode** and the target being the positive **anode**.

On striking the target, the electrons lose most (about 99%) of their energy in low-energy collisions with target atoms, resulting in a substantial heating of the target. The rest of the electron energy (usually less than 1%) reappears as X-radiation.

To deal with the excessive heat in the target the following features are employed.

- A rapidly-*rotating anode* is generally used. Its bevelled edge forms the target surface on to which the electron beam is focused. The target area under bombardment is constantly changing, thus reducing local heat concentration. (You can often hear the 'whirring' of the anode motor during the taking of an X-ray.)
- *Copper*, being an excellent heat conductor, is used for the anode mountings.
- *Oil*, circulating in the outer housing, assists with convective cooling (as well as providing electrical insulation).

Thermionic emission

When a metal or semiconductor is heated, its electrons may acquire sufficient thermal energy to escape from the surface. This process of **thermionic emission** increases with temperature: it is almost as if the electrons are being 'boiled off'. Materials with low work functions make good thermionic emitters.

X-RAYS

- **Electromagnetic radiation** of high frequencies, ($10^{17} - 10^{20}$ Hz)
- Wavelength $\lambda = \dfrac{c}{f}$
- Photon energy $E = hf$
- Diagnostic X-rays are produced in an **X-ray tube:** **tungsten target** bombarded with high speed electrons giving about 1% energy conversion.
- **Overheating** prevented using a **rotating anode** and circulating oil.

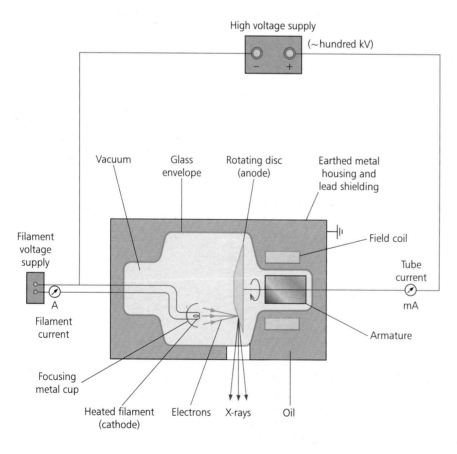

Figure 2.5 (a) A diagnostic X-ray tube.

(b) An X-ray tube out of its normal housing.

Energy exchanges in the X-ray tube – Worked example

Using a block diagram, summarise the energy exchanges that take place during the production of X-rays in an X-ray tube.

An X-ray tube is operated at a steady tube voltage of 90 kV and tube current of 80 mA. It has an efficiency of X-ray production of 0.6%. Estimate:

a) the energy of an electron reaching the target, in both J and eV.
b) the number of electrons reaching the target every second.
c) the heat generated in the target every second.

State any assumptions you make.

Figure 2.6 illustrates the major energy transformations occurring during the production of X-rays.

a) **Assuming** that the electrons are simply released from the filament during thermionic emission and have negligible initial KE, the final energy of an electron reaching the target will simply be the energy it has gained from the accelerating tube voltage V.

$$\textbf{Energy} = \textbf{charge} \times \textbf{pd}$$
$$\therefore E_{\text{electron}} = eV$$
$$= 1.6 \times 10^{-19}\,\textbf{C} \times 90 \times 10^{3}\,\textbf{V}$$
$$= 1.44 \times 10^{-14}\,\textbf{J}$$

Converting to eV:

$$\textbf{Energy} = \frac{1.44 \times 10^{-14}}{1.6 \times 10^{-19}}\,\textbf{eV}$$
$$= 90 \times 10^{3}\,\textbf{eV}$$
$$= 90\,\textbf{keV}$$

This, of course, is predictable! If an electron is accelerated through V volts, it will acquire an amount of energy in eV numerically equal to V. Thus a 90 kV tube will generate 90 keV electrons.

b) The tube current = 80 mA. Thus *every second* the charge crossing the tube = 80×10^{-3} C and since each electron carries 1.6×10^{-19} C of charge, the number of electrons crossing the tube
$$= \frac{80 \times 10^{-3}\,\text{C}}{1.6 \times 10^{-19}\,\text{C}}$$
$\therefore$ Number of electrons reaching the target per second = 5×10^{17}

c) The input power to the X-ray tube = VI

$$= 90 \times 10^{3}\,\textbf{V} \times 80 \times 10^{-3}\,\textbf{A}$$
$$= 7200\,\textbf{W}$$

The tube is only 0.6% efficient.

$\therefore$ 99.4% of the input power is wasted as heat. This amounts to

$$\textbf{0.994} \times \textbf{7200 W} = \textbf{7157 W}$$

7.16 kJ (3sf) of heat are generated in the target every second. Hence the need for effective cooling!

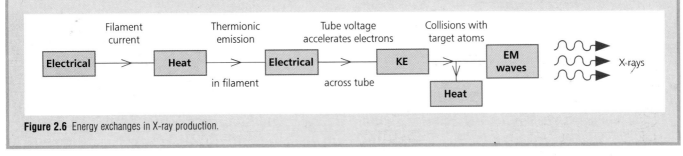

Figure 2.6 Energy exchanges in X-ray production.

X-RAY SPECTRA

The X-rays emitted from an X-ray tube display a range of energies (and hence frequencies and wavelengths). The distribution of these energies is called the **X-ray spectrum** (figure 2.7), which is usually presented as a function of photon energy (a), but can also be illustrated as a function of wavelength (b). X-rays originate through two different mechanisms and each contributes its own special features to the final spectrum.

Continuous spectrum

The incident electrons pass close to the positive nuclei of the target atoms and *decelerate (brake)* (figure 2.8(a)). The KE they lose is converted into photons of electromagnetic radiation, known as **braking radiation** (or **bremsstrahlung** from the original German). These photons have a *continuous* range of energies up to a maximum value E_{max} equal to the energy of the incoming electrons, i.e.

$$E_{max} = eV$$

where *V* is the tube voltage.

Thus, the *maximum* photon energy available from an 80 kV X-ray tube is 80 keV.

However, the *most probable* photon energy delivered, corresponding to the peak of the curve, is more likely to be around 30 keV (typically one-third to one-half of the maximum value). This gives a better idea of the *average* or *effective* energy of the continuous spectrum, which in total accounts for about 80% of the output.

Characteristic (line) spectrum

Superimposed on the continuous spectrum are a number of sharp intensity peaks constituting a **line spectrum**. The lines occur in groups, the shortest wavelength (highest energy) group being called the K-lines, the next the L-lines, and so on.

These lines are a result of bombarding electrons penetrating deep into target atoms and ejecting orbital electrons from the innermost shells (the K- and L-shells) near the nuclei (see figure 2.8(b)). Electrons from outer orbits subsequently make transitions to fill the gaps in the inner shells, thereby emitting photons whose energies are characteristic of the target atom.

Transitions terminating in the K-shell give rise to the **K-lines**, those terminating in the L-shell produce the **L-lines**, and so on. As long as the target has a high enough atomic number, *Z*, the resulting photon energies will be in the X-ray range. For example, tungsten ($Z = 74$) has K-line wavelengths around 0.02 nm, corresponding to photon energies of about 70 keV. Tube voltages of at least 70 kV are hence required to generate tungsten's characteristic K-lines.

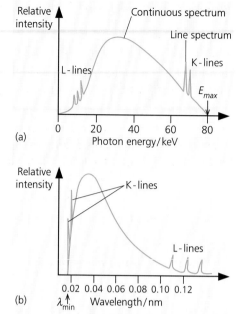

Figure 2.7 X-ray spectra: **(a)** energy representation; **(b)** wavelength representation.

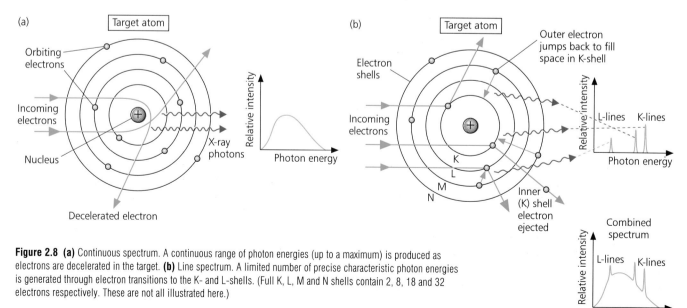

Figure 2.8 (a) Continuous spectrum. A continuous range of photon energies (up to a maximum) is produced as electrons are decelerated in the target. **(b)** Line spectrum. A limited number of precise characteristic photon energies is generated through electron transitions to the K- and L-shells. (Full K, L, M and N shells contain 2, 8, 18 and 32 electrons respectively. These are not all illustrated here.)

Factors affecting the X-ray spectrum

Tube voltage

This is controlled by the high tension supply between the anode and cathode in the X-ray tube (see figure 2.5(a)). Essentially, it determines the *energy of the electrons* as they strike the target. As tube voltage is increased (figure 2.9)

- the maximum photon energy E_{max} increases proportionally, since $E_{max} = eV$
- the peak of the continuous spectrum moves towards higher energies (the average photon energy increases)
- the total intensity (area under the curve) increases rapidly, since more of the bombarding electrons now have energies sufficient to produce X-rays. In fact

total output intensity $\propto V^2$

- more characteristic lines may appear in the spectrum.

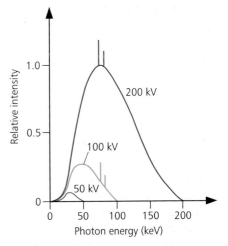

Figure 2.9 Changing the tube voltage also changes the resulting X-ray spectrum.

The **minimum wavelength** λ_{min} of the emitted radiation can be found using

$$\lambda_{min} = \frac{c}{f_{max}}$$
$$= \frac{ch}{E_{max}}$$
$$= \frac{ch}{eV}$$

Thus, as tube voltage V increases, the minimum wavelength of the radiation decreases. For example, in the case of a 110 kV X-ray tube,

maximum photon energy = $110 \times 10^3\,\text{V} \times 1.6 \times 10^{-19}\,\text{C}$

$$= 1.76 \times 10^{-14}\,\text{J}$$
$$\therefore 1.76 \times 10^{-14}\,\text{J} = hf_{max}$$
$$\therefore f_{max} = \frac{1.76 \times 10^{-14}\,\text{J}}{6.63 \times 10^{-34}\,\text{J s}}$$
$$= 2.65 \times 10^{19}\,\text{Hz}$$
$$\textbf{But } \lambda_{min} = \frac{c}{f_{max}} = \frac{3 \times 10^8\,\text{m s}^{-1}}{2.65 \times 10^{19}\,\text{s}^{-1}}$$
$$= 1.13 \times 10^{-11}\,\text{m}$$
$$= 0.0113\,\text{nm}$$

Tube current

The tube current depends on the *number of electrons* crossing the tube per second. This is controlled by the filament current, which determines the rate at which electrons are emitted from the cathode. When tube current is increased (figure 2.10):

- the shape of the spectrum remains the same
- E_{max} remains unchanged, since the maximum electron energy available remains unchanged
- the overall intensity (area under the curve) increases, since there are more electrons available to release X-ray photons. In fact:

total output intensity $\propto$ tube current

Tube current

Care must be taken to distinguish between the current flowing through the filament (the **filament current**), which is usually a few amps, and the current flowing across the evacuated X-ray tube from cathode to anode (the **tube current**), which is generally about a hundred milliamps.

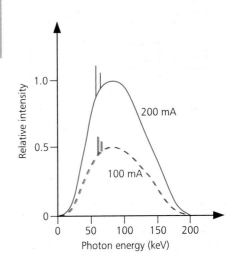

Figure 2.10 Effect of tube current on the X-ray spectrum.

Target material

An increase in target atomic number Z (figure 2.11) results in:

- an overall increase in X-ray intensity since the greater mass, size and positive charge of the target nuclei lead to a greater probability that bombarding electrons make collisions resulting in *X-ray* emission. In fact:

total output intensity $\propto Z$

- a shift of the characteristic line spectrum towards higher photon energies, since more energy is needed to expel K and L electrons from higher Z atoms
- no change in E_{max}, since the maximum electron energy available remains unchanged.

A *target material* should not only have a high melting point but also a high Z, to yield high X-ray outputs. **Tungsten**, with a melting point of 3650 K and a Z of 74, is almost universally used as a target material.

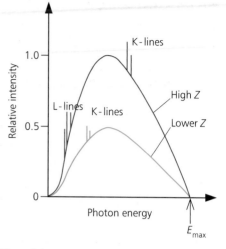

Figure 2.11 Effect of target material on the spectrum.

Filtration

If a sheet of metal or other material is placed in the path of the X-ray beam it acts as a filter, selectively absorbing more lower-energy photons than high-energy photons (figure 2.12). Such filtration thus produces:

- a change in X-ray spectrum shape with the preferential removal of lower energies
- a shift in spectrum peak towards higher energies, since the *average* photon energy is increased
- an overall reduction in X-ray output (smaller area under the curve)
- a shift in E_{min} (the minimum photon energy) towards higher energies
- no change in E_{max}.

The amount of radiation absorbed by the filter depends on photon energy, filter thickness and filter material (high-density and high-Z materials absorbing the most radiation).

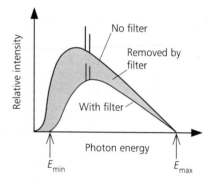

Figure 2.12 Adding a filter changes the shape of the X-ray spectrum.

X-RAY SPECTRA

- An X-ray beam contains a **spectrum** of photon energies (or frequencies).
- A **continuous spectrum** is due to electrons **decelerating** in the target. Its maximum photon energy is $E_{max} = eV$.
- A line spectrum is due to orbital electron transitions in the target. The individual lines (e.g. K-lines) have frequencies **characteristic** of the **target**.
- Factors **shaping the X-ray spectrum** are summarised in table 2.1.

Table 2.1 X-ray spectrum.

Increasing ↓	E_{max}	Total intensity	Average photon energy (~Peak position)	Characteristic lines
tube voltage	increases ($\propto V$)	increases rapidly ($\propto V^2$)	increases	more may appear
tube current	same	increases	same	same
Z (target)	same	increases	may increase	shift to higher energies
filtration	same	decreases	increases	some lower energy lines may disappear

ATTENUATION OF X-RAYS

Attenuation describes the reduction in intensity of a beam as it travels. An X-ray beam suffers attenuation for several reasons.

- Its intensity may decrease with distance from the source simply due to **divergence**. For spherical wavefronts emitted from a theoretical point source, such divergence leads to a reduction in intensity described by the inverse square law ($I \propto 1/r^2$). (This occurs even in a vacuum.)
- When the X-ray beam passes through a *medium*, the photons may also be **scattered**, causing a deflection of the energy out of the original beam direction.
- The X-ray photons may be **absorbed** in the medium thereby transferring energy to the medium.

The extent to which a medium attenuates an X-ray beam depends on

- its thickness
- the material from which it is made
- the X-ray photon energy.

> The **intensity of a beam** is the energy per second delivered through an area of 1 m², normal to the beam's direction. Its units are thus $\mathrm{J\,s^{-1}\,m^{-2}}$ or $\mathrm{W\,m^{-2}}$.

Inverse square law – Worked example

The intensity of an X-ray beam is found to be $6.4\,\mathrm{W\,mm^{-2}}$ at a distance of 0.3 m from the X-ray tube target spot. How much further away than this must a radiographer stand, in order to reduce the intensity to $0.1\,\mathrm{W\,mm^{-2}}$?

Assuming a point source, we can apply the inverse square law,

$$I \propto \frac{1}{r^2}$$

Thus, if I_1 is the intensity at a distance of r_1 from the source, and I_2 is the intensity at a distance r_2,

$$\frac{I_1}{I_2} = \frac{r_2^2}{r_1^2}$$

Using the given values

$$I_1 = 6.4\,\mathrm{W\,mm^{-2}} \text{ at } r_1 = 0.3\,\mathrm{m},$$
$$\text{and } I_2 = 0.1\,\mathrm{W\,mm^{-2}} \text{ at } r_2,$$

$$\frac{6.4\,\mathrm{W\,mm^{-2}}}{0.1\,\mathrm{W\,mm^{-2}}} = \frac{r_2^2}{0.3^2\,\mathrm{m^2}}$$

$$\therefore r_2 = 5.76\,\mathrm{m}$$

(= **distance of radiographer** *from the source*)
∴ **The radiographer must stand (5.76 – 0.3)**
= 5.46 m *further away.*

In practice, of course, there are additional methods employed by radiographers to reduce their radiation exposure (see page 113).

Attenuation of a parallel homogeneous X-ray beam

A **homogeneous**, or monoenergetic, X-ray beam contains photons of only one energy, as compared to a **heterogeneous** beam, containing several photon energies.

When a homogeneous beam passes through a medium, its intensity falls exponentially with distance covered (figure 2.13). Thus, if the intensity of the beam is initially I_0 as it enters the medium, the transmitted intensity I after travelling a thickness x is given by

$$I = I_0\,\mathrm{e}^{-\mu x} \qquad (2.1)$$

where μ is a constant known as the total linear attenuation coefficient. However thick the absorber, it is never possible to absorb an X-ray beam completely.

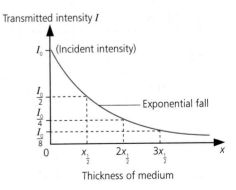

Figure 2.13 Exponential reduction in intensity of a homogeneous X-ray beam travelling through a medium.

Exponential attenuation

When a homogeneous X-ray beam passes through a medium, the fractional reduction in intensity $-\mathrm{d}I/I$ in passing through a small distance $\mathrm{d}x$ is proportional to $\mathrm{d}x$.

$$\frac{-\mathrm{d}I}{I} = \mu \, \mathrm{d}x$$

where μ is the total linear attenuation coefficient. Integrating gives:

$$[\ln I]_{I_0}^{I} = -[\mu x]_0^{x}$$

where I_0 is the incident intensity and I is the transmitted intensity after passing through a thickness x of the medium.

$$\therefore \ln I - \ln I_0 = -\mu x$$
$$\therefore I = I_0 \, e^{-\mu x} \qquad \text{as in the text.}$$

Half-value thickness

The thickness of material that reduces the intensity of an X-ray beam to half its original value is called the **half-value thickness** or **HVT** ($x_{1/2}$). Travelling through 2 HVTs reduces the intensity to a quarter of its original value and so on (see figure 2.13).

When μ is large (severe attenuation) the value of $x_{1/2}$ is correspondingly small. They are, in fact, related by the equation (see box);

$$x_{1/2} = \frac{\ln 2}{\mu} \qquad (2.2)$$

Since the distances involved are often small, $x_{1/2}$ is usually quoted in mm and μ in mm^{-1}.

Half-value thickness

$$I = I_0 \, e^{-\mu x}$$

When the beam has travelled a distance $x_{1/2}$, I is reduced to $\frac{I_0}{2}$. Thus,

$$\frac{I_0}{2} = I_0 \, e^{-\mu x_{1/2}}$$
$$\therefore \ \tfrac{1}{2} = e^{-\mu x_{1/2}}$$
$$\therefore \ 2 = e^{\mu x_{1/2}}$$
$$\therefore \ \ln 2 = \mu x_{1/2}$$
$$\therefore \ x_{1/2} = \frac{\ln 2}{\mu} = \frac{0.693}{\mu}$$

Attenuation of a homogeneous X-ray beam – Worked example

The half-value thickness of a filter for 30 keV photons is 1.5 mm.
a) What is the linear attenuation coefficient for this beam in this filter?
b) What thickness of filter is needed to reduce the beam intensity to
   i) 1/8 of its original value
   ii) 1/10 of its original value?

a) The linear attenuation coefficient μ is given by

$$\mu = \frac{\ln 2}{x_{1/2}}$$
$$= \frac{\ln 2}{1.5 \,\text{mm}}$$
$$\therefore \mu = 0.46 \,\text{mm}^{-1} \qquad \textbf{(2sf)}$$

b) i) In order to reduce the beam intensity to 1/8 of the initial value, 3 half-value thicknesses are required (figure 2.14).

$$\therefore \ \textbf{Filter thickness needed} = 3 \times 1.5 \,\text{mm}$$
$$= 4.5 \,\text{mm.}$$

ii) This is more difficult, and we need to apply the equation

$$I = I_0 e^{-\mu x}$$
$$\frac{I}{I_0} = \frac{1}{10} \text{ and } \mu = 0.46 \,\text{mm}^{-1}$$
$$\therefore \ \frac{1}{10} = e^{-0.46x}$$

where x is in mm

$$\therefore \ \ln 0.1 = -0.46x$$
$$\therefore \ x = \frac{-\ln 0.1}{0.46} = 5.0 \,\text{mm} \qquad \textbf{(2sf)}$$

Thus the filter thickness needed is 5.0 mm

Heterogeneous beams: quality and hardness

Heterogeneous beams contain a range of photon energies, and in passing through a medium these are attenuated by varying amounts. Lower energy photons suffer more attenuation than higher energy ones, so as the beam passes through the medium, it loses more and more of its *lower* energy photons. The remaining photons are now of *higher average energy* and are relatively more penetrating. The **half-value thickness** $x_{1/2}$ therefore increases as the beam progresses.

The **quality** of an X-ray beam describes its **penetrating power**. A beam containing higher energy photons is more penetrating than one with lower energies, and is said to be of better quality. Such a beam has a larger value of $x_{1/2}$, since it travels a longer way through the medium before its intensity is halved.

As a heterogeneous beam passes through a medium, its quality gradually increases, a process described as '**hardening**'. It becomes relatively more penetrating, by increasing its *percentage* of high-energy photons, and its half value thickness increases.

The quality, hardness or penetrating power of a beam may be improved by

- increasing the X-ray tube voltage, or
- using a filter

as either of these will tend to shift the peak of the photon energy distribution curve (see figures 2.9 and 2.12) to higher energies and thus *on average* increase photon energy.

Heterogeneous beam attenuation – Worked example

Figure 2.14 shows the reduction in intensity of a heterogeneous X-ray beam from an 80 kV X-ray tube as the beam passes through an aluminium filter.
a) State, giving reasons, whether or not the labelled curve is exponential.
b) Identify which of the other curves (1) or (2) might describe the attenuation of
  i) an identical beam passing through a lead filter, and
  ii) a beam, from a 120 kV X-ray tube, passing through an aluminium filter.

a) Since the beam is heterogeneous, the half-value thickness, HVT, increases (or the attenuation constant decreases) with the distance x covered. Hence, the curve is not exactly exponential.

b) i) Lead has a higher value of both density and atomic number and will lead to greater attenuation. The curve will fall more steeply and have a smaller HVT. The answer is thus (1).
  ii) A 120 kV X-ray tube produces on average higher energy X-ray photons. These are less easily attenuated in the aluminium, demanding a greater HVT. The answer is (2).

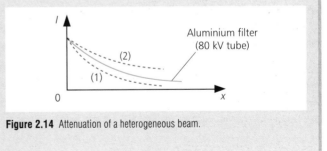

Figure 2.14 Attenuation of a heterogeneous beam.

The mass attenuation coefficient

The attenuation of a heterogeneous X-ray beam in a medium is complicated since there are so many variables! Density (ρ) and atomic number (Z) of the medium, as well as photon energy (E), all influence the attenuation coefficient μ.

However, since for a given E and Z, $\mu \propto \rho$, density can automatically be 'allowed for' by defining a new coefficient

$$\mu_{\mathrm{m}} = \frac{\mu}{\rho} \quad (\mathrm{m^2\,kg^{-1}})$$

called the **mass attenuation coefficient**. This then describes the attenuation per unit mass of material traversed and depends only on Z and E.

The coefficient μ_{m} tends to

- increase with increasing Z
- increase with decreasing E (lower energy photons are more easily attenuated) (see table 2.2 on page 39).

Measurement of half-value thickness

The HVT of a particular homogeneous X-ray beam in a chosen material may be determined experimentally by placing various thicknesses (x) of the material in the path of the selected beam, and measuring the transmitted intensity (I), for example, using a Geiger tube. Since

$$I = I_0 e^{-\mu x}$$
$$\ln I = \ln I_0 - \mu x$$

and a plot of $\ln I$ against x yields a straight line of slope $-\mu$. Once μ is found, $x_{1/2}$ can be calculated using equation 2.2:

$$x_{1/2} = \frac{\ln 2}{\mu}$$

For example, a beam of 80 keV X-ray photons has a HVT of 1 mm in copper, whilst a beam of 1 MeV γ-ray photons, like that from a cobalt-60 source, has a HVT of 10 mm in lead.

ATTENUATION MECHANISMS

The *way* in which an X-ray beam is attenuated in a medium depends largely on the energy of its photons and the medium involved. The most important attenuation mechanisms in body tissue (figure 2.15) are described below.

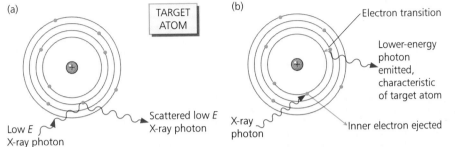
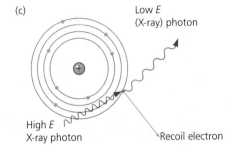

Figure 2.15 Attenuation mechanisms: **(a)** simple scatter; **(b)** photoelectric effect; **(c)** Compton scatter.

Simple scatter

The incident photon energy (E) is much less than the energy required to remove an electron from its atom (the binding energy, E_b). The photon is simply deflected without change of energy. It is scattered **elastically**.

Photoelectric effect

The photon (E slightly greater than E_b) gives up *all* of its energy to an **inner orbital** electron, thereby ejecting it from its atom. The excited atom subsequently returns to its ground state with the emission of characteristic photons, most of which are of relatively low energy and are immediately absorbed in the material itself. The ejected **photoelectron** ionises further atoms along its path until its (often considerable) kinetic energy has been dissipated.

Compton scatter

E is much greater than E_b and only *part* of the photon energy is given up during the interaction with an **outer (valence) electron**, which is effectively 'free'. The photon continues in a different direction with diminished energy, and the electron (known as a **recoil electron**) dissipates its energy through ionisation.

Attenuation of X-rays in the body

Table 2.2 Attenuation mechanisms.

Mechanism	Variation of μ_m with E (photon energy)	Variation of μ_m with Z (atomic number)	Energy range in which dominant in soft tissue
simple scatter	$\propto 1/E$	$\propto Z^2$	1–20 keV
photoelectric effect	$\propto 1/E^3$	$\propto Z^3$	1-30 keV
Compton scatter	falls very gradually with E	independent	30 keV–20 MeV

Table 2.2 summarises how the mass attenuation coefficient μ_m (attenuation per unit mass of the medium) varies with **photon energy** and **atomic number** of the medium. Figure 2.16 further illustrates how different attenuation mechanisms dominate at different photon energies.

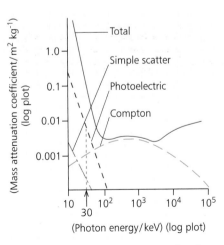

Figure 2.16 The different mechanisms contribute in varying ways to the total attenuation. (The increase at high energies is due to another mechanism called pair production.)

In **radiography**, we need to *distinguish* between, or *differentiate* various body tissues. In other words, we require **contrast**. Looking at table 2.2, which attenuation mechanism do you think would give the best contrast?

The answer is the **photoelectric effect**, since it depends on the *cube* of the *atomic number* of the medium. For example, the average values of *Z* for fat, muscle and bone are 5.9, 7.4 and 13.9 respectively (making their Z^3 values 205, 405 and 2686). This leads to a photoelectric attenuation in bone about 11 times greater than that in surrounding tissue.

Simple scatter is just a nuisance and a dose hazard, since it gives rise to blurring of the radiographic image and low-energy absorption in the patient's skin, possibly resulting in skin cancer.

Compton scatter is useless, as it is independent of *Z*!

Having chosen the photoelectric effect as the preferred mechanism, what **photon energy** would you now select to maximise this type of attenuation?

Referring to figure 2.16, the optimum photon energy for radiography is around **30 keV**, giving photoelectric absorption predominance over the other mechanisms. In order to produce a beam in which 30 keV photons are the most probable, an X-ray tube voltage of about 80–100 kV is best, together with some filtration (see figure 2.8).

Very much in contrast, deep therapy (see page 99) with its higher intensities, should be avoided in this energy range, because of the potential danger to bone. Energies above 30 keV (and more commonly in the range 0.5–5 MeV) are hence selected for radiotherapy, so that Compton scatter (with its independence of *Z*) is the predominant attenuation mechanism.

X-ray filters

In order to apply *just* the optimum energy photons, we need to employ **filters** to remove the useless and potentially damaging low-energy photons. These never reach the X-ray film and are simply absorbed in the patient's skin, possibly causing cancer.

The primary beam of X-rays emitted from an X-ray tube passes through the glass wall of the tube, a layer of oil and a shield aperture before emerging, so that some absorption of the lower-energy photons always takes place. This **inherent filtration** of a diagnostic tube may be equivalent, for instance, to that produced by about 0.5–1.0 mm of aluminium. Despite inherent filtration, the X-ray beam still contains a high proportion of low-energy radiation that has to be removed. The beam needs to be **hardened**: an extra filter is required. In diagnostic work, filters of a few millimetres of aluminium are normally used.

Filter materials

Suitable filters consist of materials in which photoelectric attenuation dominates in the given energy range. In diagnostic radiography and superficial radiotherapy, aluminium (*Z* = 13) closely matches body attenuation, and is the common choice. For the higher energies employed in deep therapy, aluminium absorbs too much by Compton scatter and higher-*Z* filters are used of copper (*V*~120–200 kV), tin (*V*~ 200–400 kV), lead (*V*~800–2000 kV), or gold (*V* above ~2000 kV). Often, composite filters are used so that the required attenuation is achieved and any characteristic radiation emitted in one material is absorbed in the other.

Beam Attenuation

- **Attenuation** (reduction in intensity) depends on the medium and the photon energies – **higher-energies** are attenuated less.
- The **penetrating power** of a beam is measured by its **half-value thickness** $x_{1/2}$ in a material, (the thickness of medium required to reduce the intensity by half).
- A **homogeneous beam** contains a single photon energy and its attenuation is exponential, $I = I_0 e^{-\mu x}$
- A **heterogeneous beam** consists of many photon energies. A **filter** makes such a beam **harder**, of **better quality**, and relatively **more penetrating**.
- **Attenuation** is due to: 'inverse square law' divergence, **simple scatter** (hazardous, (skin cancer), and blurs the image), **absorption** in the medium, due to **photoelectric absorption** or **Compton scatter**.
- **Photoelectric absorption** gives the best contrast in diagnosis ($\propto Z^3$).

THE RADIOGRAPHIC IMAGE (THE 'X-RAY')

What we actually see in an 'X-ray' is a 'shadow image'. X-rays pass through the body to varying extents and **blacken** the photographic film or plate (figure 2.17).

Table 2.3 X-ray attenuation.

Medium	Attenuation	Appearance on film
air	negligible	black
fat	small	dark grey
other soft tissues	medium	grey
bone	high	white

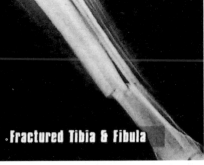

Figure 2.17 X-ray showing fractured tibia and fibula.

The visibility of structures and disease depends upon the **differential absorption** of X-rays by different body tissues (table 2.3). Sometimes, the **natural contrast** provided by the body structures is inadequate, in which case artificial **contrast agents** are required. These are usually compounds of high proton number elements, such as barium (gastrointestinal tract studies) and iodine (circulatory system investigations).

At present, the X-ray beam cannot be focused, like light or electron beams, and several techniques are employed to give as sharp an image as possible.

Factors affecting image quality

There are many factors, some conflicting, which influence the quality of the radiographic image formed after an X-ray beam passes through the body. The major aims are to produce

- *sharp* images, by increasing resolution and reducing blur
- *good contrast* in the image, by distinguishing clearly between different body materials.

Tube voltage

This is generally in the range 60–125 kV, with approximately 70 kV being the most commonly used (table 2.4). For good contrast, it is important for photoelectric attenuation to dominate (see page 40) and these voltages produce the optimum photon energies required.

As tube voltage is increased, there is a tendency for photoelectric attenuation to fall and Compton scatter to rise in importance, leading to a reduction in contrast. Care must be taken, therefore, to select a high enough tube voltage to penetrate the structure under examination, but not too high to reduce valuable contrast. For example, a high tube voltage would be necessary when examining the chest of a fat person, whilst in breast examinations, where small differences in attenuation can be crucial, much lower tube voltages would be required.

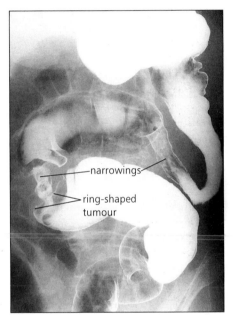

Figure 2.18 A barium enema is given to the patient to image the bowel. The barium absorbs the X-ray and appears white, indicating the shape of the bowel. Here, there are two clear narrowings, one due to a ring-shaped tumour.

Table 2.4 Typical examination parameters*.

Examination	Voltage/kV	Current/mA	Exposure time/s
chest	80	400	0.01
pelvis/abdomen	70	400	0.10
skull	70	400	0.05
hand	60	300	0.01
breast	30	300	0.25

* Note: These values vary considerably from hospital to hospital, since they are very dependent on the speed of film used.

Tube current

An increase in tube current results in a greater intensity of both incident and transmitted beams, leading to more blackening of the film. Although this improves contrast, it is at the expense of larger patient absorbed doses and increased heating of the target.

Exposure time

Like tube current, increase in exposure times leads to more blackening of the film and although this improves radiographic contrast, such times are limited by:

- patient absorbed dose
- overheating of the target
- movement blur, which is produced by (often involuntary) movement of the examined structure during exposure.

Since both tube current (mA) and exposure time (s) effect the X-ray exposure, it is common practice for the radiographer to select a 'combined' current × exposure setting, measured in mAs.

Beam size

Narrow beams are preferred in radiography, since the random scatter that inevitably increases with wider beams blurs the radiographic image.

The cross-section of an X-ray beam can be controlled by a beam definer or diaphragm. Figure 2.19(a) and (b) illustrates an adjustable diaphragm, consisting of two pairs of lead sheets, which can move at right angles to each other, so that a rectangular cross-section can be defined. Another simple beam definer is a section of a cone as shown in figure 2.19(c).

Such designs often incorporate a light box to assist with alignment of the beam. A lamp and mirror are positioned so that a light beam of exactly the same size, shape and direction as the X-ray beam illuminates the patient. The radiographer can then clearly see the region to be exposed and adjust it if necessary.

Filtration

Filters reduce unwanted low-energy radiation and scatter. This results in an increase in the average photon energy (the peak of the relative intensity curve moves to higher photon energies (see figure 2.12) allowing photoelectric attenuation to dominate, and decreasing simple scatter. Both contrast and sharpness of image are improved.

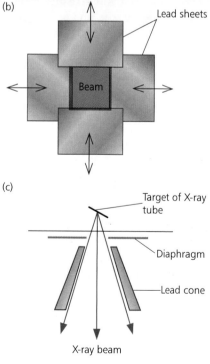

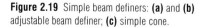

Figure 2.19 Simple beam definers: **(a)** and **(b)** adjustable beam definer; **(c)** simple cone.

Focal spot size

If the X-rays originated from a point focus (figure 2.20(a)) a clear shadow image would be formed with sharp edges.

In practice, however, X-rays originate from a small *area* of the target, known as the extended focus or focal spot, onto which the electron beam is focused (figure 2.20(b)). Each point on the focal spot produces its own slightly different image on the film. The result is a central region of full shadow, the **umbra**, surrounded by a blurred region of partial shadow or **penumbra**.

The extent of this **penumbra, or geometric, blur** of the image may be reduced by

- positioning the film close to the patient
- reducing the size of the focal spot. This is achieved by using a sharply angled (~17°) target (figure 2.20(c)) thereby reducing the **effective** or **projected** focal spot area.

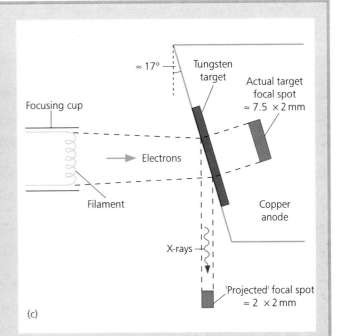

(c)

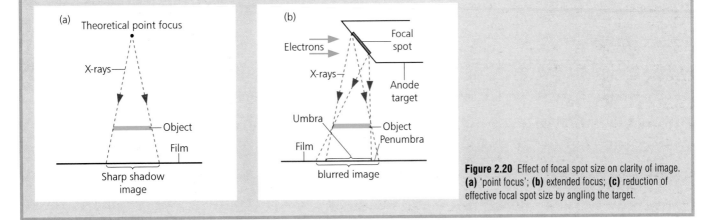

(a) Theoretical point focus
X-rays
Object
Film
Sharp shadow image

(b) Electrons
Focal spot
X-rays
Anode target
Umbra
Object
Penumbra
Film
blurred image

Figure 2.20 Effect of focal spot size on clarity of image. **(a)** 'point focus'; **(b)** extended focus; **(c)** reduction of effective focal spot size by angling the target.

Use of a grid

To reduce further the blurring of images caused by scattered radiation, a grid of lead strips may be used directly in front of the film (figure 2.21). Direct, or primary, radiation reaches the film through the gaps, whereas scattered radiation is intercepted by the grid. If two 'crossed grids' are used at right angles to each other, almost complete elimination of unwanted scatter occurs.

The formation of an image of the lead strips on the film, sometimes referred to as grid lines, may be prevented by moving the grid slowly across the film during exposure.

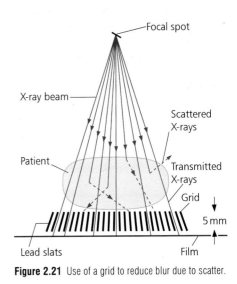

Figure 2.21 Use of a grid to reduce blur due to scatter.

Intensifying screens

Most (about 97%) of the X-rays falling on a photographic film pass straight through without any interaction. The film alone is not, therefore, a very sensitive method of detecting X-rays!

Lower-energy **light photons**, on the other hand, are more readily absorbed by the film. Hence, a common solution to improving sensitivity is to use fluorescent screens that absorb the X-radiation and re-emit visible radiation in a pattern duplicating that of the original X-ray beam.

In the simple intensifying screen cassette (figures 2.22(a) and (b)) two fluorescent screens (fluorescent crystals bonded to white plastic) are placed either side of a double-sided film. A layer of felt padding helps to ensure good screen-film contact, and the whole is contained in a lightproof plastic envelope called a cassette. The metal backing to the cassette provides some radiation protection for operational personnel and reduces scatter back into the film 'sandwich' from the couch below.

X-rays from the patient penetrate the film and two fluorescent screens. Although a slight X-ray image is directly produced on the film emulsions, the main film blackening results from the *light* emitted in the adjacent fluorescent screens (figure 2.22(c)).

Modern screens can give intensification factors of up to 250. The increased image intensity then permits shorter exposure times, and reduced radiation doses to the patient, but conversely some detail is inevitably lost due to the diffusion of the fluorescent light. Typically, the resolution achievable using intensifying screens is about 0.25–0.5 mm, whilst direct exposure film can yield better than 0.1 mm.

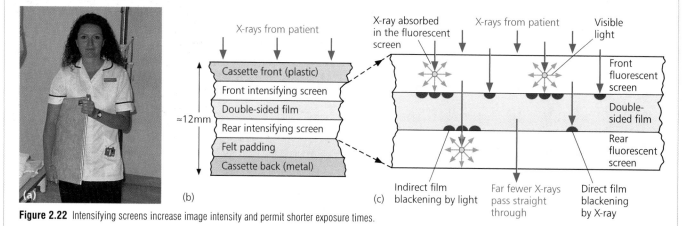

Figure 2.22 Intensifying screens increase image intensity and permit shorter exposure times.

Fluorescence

When ionising radiation, such as X-radiation, is absorbed in certain materials, called **scintillators** or **phosphors**, the energy raises some of their atoms to excited states. These excited atoms subsequently decay to their ground state re-emitting the energy in the form of visible light photons. Using a microscope, these may be observed as minute flashes of light appearing at random, and they are known as **scintillations**. If the emission of light occurs without significant time delay, the process is referred to as **fluorescence**.

IMAGE CLARITY

- **Contrast** (extent to which different tissues are **distinguished**) is improved by:
  adjusting the **tube voltage** to maximise **photoelectric absorption**,
  increasing the **tube current** and **exposure time**, giving greater film blackening,
  using **artificial contrast media** (e.g. barium).
- **Resolution** (**fineness of detail** observable) improves with:
  shorter exposure times, to reduce movement blur,
  increased filtration (less simple scatter),
  narrower beams, and a **grid**, reducing scatter,
  finer grain film.

DIAGNOSTIC APPLICATIONS OF X-RAYS

Skeletal system

A standard radiograph is usually the first course of action when a patient is suffering from a suspected bone injury. The *excellent natural contrast* provided by bone produces clear images with good resolution. Two views at right angles to each other are generally required and can lead to the diagnosis of fractures, dislocations, spinal injuries and so on. Other abnormalities, ranging from tumours and cysts in the spine to arthritis (figure 2.23), can also be indicated.

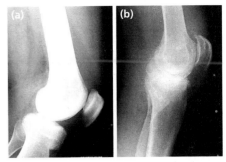

Figure 2.23 Two very different knees. (**a**) A normal knee, displaying smooth bone surfaces. (**b**) A knee with severe arthritis. Note the irregular bone surfaces and evidence of increased bone growth.

Soft tissues

The common 'X-ray' is not ideal for investigating soft tissue, since the *natural contrast is poor*. The slight exception is **fat**, with its lower Z-value, which *can* be distinguished from other soft tissues. An ordinary radiograph is thus sometimes used to assess fat-related conditions, such as obesity.

Otherwise, **artificial contrast media**, such as a '**barium meal**' are required. The patient is either asked to swallow a thick suspension containing barium sulphate, or is given a barium enema (figure 2.18). Barium has a much higher value of Z than body tissues, and is therefore 'opaque' to diagnostic X-rays. Its passage through the gastrointestinal tract is thus easily monitored, yielding information about the condition of the system.

Alternatively, very good soft tissue resolution may be achieved using **CT** (**computed tomography**), as detailed on the Web page. Brain disorders, ruptured spinal discs or soft tissue damage associated with a bone fracture can clearly be investigated.

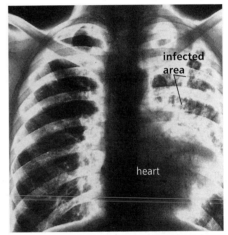

Figure 2.24 This X-ray of the lungs of a tubercular patient shows patchy areas where the disease has damaged the lung.

The chest

A standard chest X-ray is the commonest means of detecting lung cancer and other abnormalities (figure 2.24). Difficulties sometimes arise due to the inevitable obstruction of the heart.

Breast studies (mammography)

High resolution, low dose and enhanced contrast between similar soft tissues are the major requirements of a breast-screening unit to detect cancer (see figure 5.25 on page 113).

Breast screening

To provide the high resolution demanded, special mammographic film cassettes are used, containing *single*-emulsion film and one intensifying screen (see box page 44).

Contrast is improved using low tube-voltages (26–32 kV) with a molybdenum target, to ensure the predominance of photoelectric attenuation and thus good tissue differentiation. A molybdenum filter is used to 'sharpen' the beam, since aluminium would cause excessive beam hardening.

A relatively high tube current is used in order to reduce exposure time and hence movement blur. A very small focal spot (approximately 0.2 mm) further improves clarity.

The interpretation of mammograms is a repetitive task that requires attention to minute detail. Some positive cases inevitably slip through the net (maybe as much as 10–30%) and current developments include the use of computer-aided analysis, followed by the second opinion of the radiologist.

Although mammographic screening of women aged 50 and above is advised by all major medical organisations and has been shown to reduce breast cancer mortality by 20–40%, it is still debatable whether the screening of younger women is beneficial.

Circulatory system

An artificial contrast medium, typically an organic iodine compound, is injected into the blood vessel to be examined. The structure and effective flow diameter of both arteries and veins can be examined, allowing the diagnosis of blood vessel blockages and heart disease (figure 2.25).

Dental studies

Most dental practices now have small X-ray units, to investigate problems with the overcrowding or uneven growth of teeth, particularly in juveniles, or with the growth of wisdom teeth. Surgery or orthodontal treatment may then be recommended.

Foreign bodies

It is amazing what people, particularly children, will swallow! A standard radiograph can help to identify the shape and position of such objects to assist with their removal. It can also provide a screening service for MRI examinations (see page 95), where the presence of magnetic or metallic implants can be hazardous.

ADVANTAGES AND DISADVANTAGES OF DIAGNOSTIC X-RAYS

Advantages

1 A simple radiograph is relatively **cheap** and **easy** to obtain.
2 No elaborate preparation or screening is necessary, making the examination **swift**.
3 **Good bone resolution**, making it ideal for accident investigations.
4 **Relatively mobile** (lung and breast screening units), and can be compact (dental units).
5 **CT** offers good soft-tissue contrast, flexibility and 3-D imaging.

Disadvantages

1 Potentially **harmful** due to ionising radiation (risk of cancer).
2 **Electrical dangers** associated with high-voltage supplies.
3 **Poor soft-tissue resolution** (unless CT used).
4 Use of contrast media can be **unpleasant** and hazardous.
5 Dose is **cumulative**.

See also page 3 for a full comparison of the different imaging modalities.

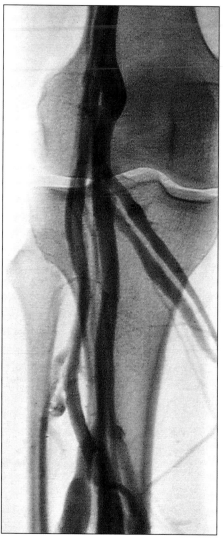

Figure 2.25 The blood vessels in the leg are seen clearly using an artificial contrast medium.

APPLICATIONS

- Due to **excellent natural contrast** in **bone**, fractures, dislocations, skull and spinal injuries are diagnosed.
- **Soft tissues** are not easily distinguished. **Artificial contrast media** (e.g. barium) are needed for stomach and bowel studies.
- Lung cancer is identified using a standard **chest X-ray**.
- **Breast screening** detects early cancer.
- Small portable **dental** X-ray units used to investigate the growth of wisdom and other teeth.

QUESTIONS

Throughout, assume $e = -1.6 \times 10^{-19}$ C,
$h = 6.63 \times 10^{-34}$ J s, $c = 3.0 \times 10^8$ m s^{-1}

1 a An X-ray tube with a tungsten target is operated at a peak voltage of 80 kV, without additional filtration. Show graphically how the intensity of the resulting X-radiation varies with photon energy, and explain the main features of the graph.

b Calculate the maximum energy of emitted X-ray photons in
i electron-volts
ii joules.

2 a Discuss the parts played by conduction, convection and radiation in the cooling of a diagnostic X-ray tube.

b It is found that the X-ray spectrum emitted from a certain X-ray tube has a minimum wavelength of 0.02 nm. Explain why no shorter wavelengths are observed. At what voltage is this tube operating?

3 a Describe the energy exchanges that occur during the production of X-rays in an X-ray tube.

b An X-ray tube is operated with a voltage of 65 kV and a tube (beam) current of 300 mA. It has an efficiency of X-ray production of 0.6%. Estimate
i at what rate the machine transforms energy (the input power)
ii the number of electrons hitting the target every second
iii the rate of production of heat in the target
iv the energy per second carried away by the X-ray beam (the output power).

4 a Explain carefully the effects of:
i tube voltage
ii tube current
iii target material
on the X-ray spectrum derived from an X-ray tube.

b An X-ray tube operates at a tube voltage of 80 kV and tube current of 150 mA. It produces an X-ray beam of initial cross-sectional area 2 mm^2, with an efficiency of 1%. Find the initial intensity of the beam.

5 a Define the half-value thickness of a beam of X-radiation, passing through an absorber. Describe briefly how this value could be measured experimentally.

b An X-ray beam of intensity 30 MW m^{-2} passes through an aluminium filter. The half-value thickness of this beam in aluminium is 1.5 mm. Find the intensity of the beam after it has travelled through a filter of thickness
i 4.5 mm
ii 5.0 mm.

6 a Describe the physical processes responsible for the attenuation of a diagnostic X-ray beam in the body. Discuss the relative importance of these mechanisms:
i for beams of different energies
ii in different materials of the body.

b The intensity of the beam emerging from an X-ray tube is 0.5 MW m^{-2} at a distance of 0.2 m from the tube's focal spot. Assuming the latter may be treated as a point source, estimate

i the beam intensity at a distance of 2.0 m from it
ii the distance away from it where the beam intensity is 0.1 MW m^{-2}.

7 a Explain what is meant by the **contrast** in a radiograph and indicate how it can be optimised.

b The half-value thickness of 30 keV X-rays in aluminium is 2.4 mm. A homogeneous 30 keV beam, of intensity 0.4 MW m^{-2} passes through an aluminium filter. Find
i the linear attenuation coefficient of aluminium for this beam
ii the thickness of filter required to reduce the beam intensity to 60 kW m^{-2}
iii the emerging beam intensity if the filter is 4 mm thick.

8 a Describe photoelectric absorption and Compton scatter. State and explain their relative importance in diagnosis and therapy.

b A 200 kV X-ray tube has a current of 150 mA. It produces an X-ray beam of diameter 1.5 mm. The efficiency of the tube is 0.6%. Calculate the intensity of the beam leaving the tube. State one assumption you have made in your calculation.

(ULEAC 1996)

9 a With reference to an X-ray beam explain the terms
i intensity
ii quality
iii hardness
iv penetrating power.

b Describe how each is affected by the passage of the beam through a filter.

c Calculate the ratio of the transmitted to the incident intensities of an X-ray beam travelling through an aluminium filter 2 mm thick, if the half-value thickness is 3 mm.

10 a Describe how the quality of a radiographic image depends on:
i X-ray tube current
ii exposure time
iii size of the focal spot.

b When attempting to improve image quality, are any of these factors conflicting?

c Describe and account for the appearance on an X-ray film of bone, soft tissue and air spaces.

11 Explain and distinguish between the terms
a sharpness
b contrast
when used to indicate the quality of an X-ray image. In **each** case, state 3 factors upon which it depends.

12 In a breast-screening unit, an X-ray tube is operated at a relatively **low tube voltage** of 28 kV, quite a **high tube current** of 400 mA and employs a very **small focal spot size**. Explain how these features of X-ray production lead to the optimum means of diagnosing breast cancer.

Radioisotopes in diagnosis

Radioisotopes find many applications in medicine, ranging from the destruction of cancer to the powering of artificial pacemakers. In this chapter, however, we shall investigate only their diagnostic uses.

A radioisotope is something that emits α-, β- or γ-radiation spontaneously. If such a substance is taken into the body, it still emits its radiation, giving us a method of locating where it is: it acts like a small 'beacon'. The selected radioisotope is 'attached' to a convenient chemical compound and administered to the body. It then makes its way through the system, leaving its trail of radiation as it goes, thus permitting us to trace its path. Often, it will concentrate in a particular organ of the body, allowing detailed imaging of that structure (figure 3.1).

To enable such a **radioactive tracer** to be detected outside the body, the radiation it emits needs to be relatively penetrating, making γ-emitters preferable. Sophisticated γ-**cameras** are employed to detect the signals, which are then used to build up a 'picture' of the distribution of the radioisotope in the body.

In previous chapters, we have seen how ultrasound and X-rays may be used to image the body. **Radioisotope imaging** is yet another way of 'seeing into the body', but this time we are seeing something different. We are observing how the body *functions*. It would be meaningful to 'take an X-ray' or perform an ultrasound scan on a dead body: we could still learn something about body structure. However, a radioactive tracer investigation would be a waste of time, since the body is no longer *functioning!*

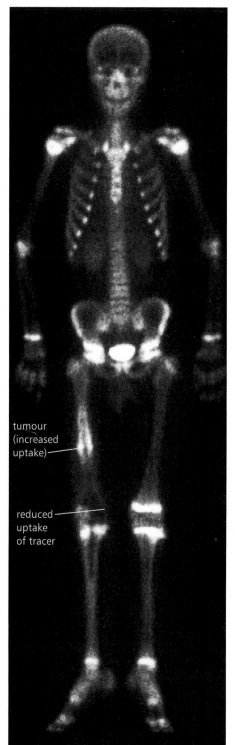

tumour (increased uptake)

reduced uptake of tracer

Figure 3.1 A whole body scan showing the accumulation of tracer in bone. This young teenager displays typical increased activity in the joints, due to rapid growth, but also shows a tumour in the leg. Note the lack of uptake in the knee below the tumour area.

SOME BASIC RADIOACTIVITY

Terms and notation

The conventional way to represent an atom of element X is $^A_Z X$, where:

A = **mass number** (or **nucleon** number) = number of nucleons (neutrons and protons) in the nucleus

Z = **atomic number** (or **proton** number) = number of protons in the nucleus.

All atoms of a particular element have the same Z, although they may contain different numbers of neutrons, giving them different values of A. Atoms with the same atomic number, but with different numbers of neutrons, are called **isotopes** of an element. Another name for an isotope is a **nuclide**.

Many elements have several naturally-occurring isotopes, but only a limited number are **stable** (there is a negligible chance that they will decay). The rest, because their neutron-proton ratio is beyond certain limits, are **unstable, or radioactive**, and **decay** to a stable form by emission of particles and photons from the nucleus.

A **radionuclide** is a nuclide that spontaneously undergoes radioactive decay, by emitting either α-, β- or γ-radiation. For example, $^{131}_{53} I$ is an **isotope of iodine**. It is a **radionuclide** that decays by the emission of β- and γ-radiation.

For the rest of the chapter, the term radionuclide will be used, in preference to radioisotope, because of its wider popularity.

Radioactive decay

Radioactive nuclei decay spontaneously. They either 'go' or 'don't go' *randomly*: the process cannot be speeded up or slowed down. Since it *is* a random process, the laws of statistics prevail. The more radioactive atoms there are in a sample, the greater the probability that a decay will occur in a set time interval. Mathematically: the number of atoms that decay per second $\frac{dN}{dt}$ is directly proportional to the number of radioactive atoms N present in the sample at that time, that is:

$$\frac{dN}{dt} \propto -N$$

(the minus is necessary because the number of radioactive atoms is *decreasing*).

$$\therefore \frac{dN}{dt} = -\lambda N \qquad \textbf{(3.1)}$$

where λ is the decay constant. This then leads to the standard equation for radioactive decay, namely

$$N = N_0 e^{-\lambda t} \qquad \textbf{(3.2)}$$

where N_0 is the original number of radioactive atoms in the sample, at the time $t = 0$ s (see box). The number of radioactive nuclei N **remaining** after a time t thus decreases **exponentially** (figure 3.2).

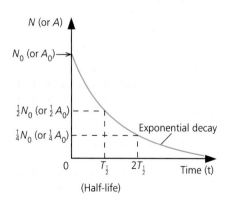

Figure 3.2 Radioactive decay is exponential.

Radioactive decay

For the random process of radioactive decay,

$$\frac{\mathrm{d}N}{\mathrm{d}t} = -\lambda N$$

$$\frac{\mathrm{d}N}{N} = -\lambda \; \mathrm{d}t$$

$$\therefore \int \frac{\mathrm{d}N}{N} = -\lambda \int \mathrm{d}t$$

integrating gives $\qquad [\ln N]^{N}_{N_0} = [-\lambda t]^{t}_{0}$

$$\therefore \quad \frac{N}{N_0} = e^{-\lambda t}$$

$$\therefore \quad N = N_0 e^{-\lambda t}$$

Thus, a radioisotope decays exponentially as shown in figure 3.2.

Since the **activity** A of a source is defined as the number of decays per second,

$$A = \frac{-\mathrm{d}N}{\mathrm{d}t}$$

$$A = \frac{-\mathrm{d}[N_0 e^{-\lambda t}]}{\mathrm{d}t}$$

$$A = \lambda N_0 e^{-\lambda t}$$

If the source has an activity A_0 at the time $t = 0$,

$$A_0 = \lambda N_0$$

$$\therefore \; A = A_0 e^{-\lambda t}$$

which is an exponential fall, identical to that illustrated in figure 3.2.

Activity

The **activity** A of a source is the **rate of decay** $\dfrac{-\mathrm{d}N}{\mathrm{d}t}$ of its radioactive atoms (the negative sign indicates that N is *decreasing*). It is measured in becquerels (Bq) where 1 Bq is equal to 1 disintegration per second. This is a common practical unit, since most experimental procedures involve measuring sample activities. However, it is a very small unit, and MBq ($\times 10^6$) or GBq ($\times 10^9$) are frequently used.

It may be shown (see box) that the activity decays exponentially with time, just like the number of radioactive atoms, i.e.

$$A = A_0 e^{-\lambda t} \qquad (3.3)$$

where A_0 is the initial activity at time $t = 0$, and A is the activity *remaining* after a time t.

Activity – Worked example

The activity of a sample of radioactive material falls from 9.0 MBq to 2.0 MBq in 3 minutes. Find its radioactive decay constant, λ.

Using $\qquad\qquad A = A_0 e^{-\lambda t}$

and substituting $\quad A_0 = 9 \times 10^6 \, \mathrm{Bq}, A = 2 \times 10^6 \, \mathrm{Bq}, t = 3 \times 60 \, \mathrm{s} = 180 \, \mathrm{s}$,

$$2 \times 10^6 \, \mathrm{Bq} = 9 \times 10^6 \, \mathrm{Bq} \times e^{-\lambda \times 180}$$

$$\therefore \frac{2}{9} = e^{-180 \times \lambda}$$

$$\therefore \ln\left(\frac{2}{9}\right) = -180 \times \lambda$$

$$-1.50 = -180 \times \lambda$$

$$\therefore \; \lambda = 0.0084 \, \mathrm{s}^{-1} \qquad \textbf{(2sf)}$$

Half-life

The **half-life $T_{1/2}$**, of a radionuclide is defined as the *average* time taken for the activity to fall to half its initial value, or alternatively as the *average* time taken for half the radioactive atoms to disintegrate (see figure 3.2).

$$A = A_0e^{-\lambda t} \quad \text{or} \quad N = N_0e^{-\lambda t}$$

After one half–life $T_{1/2}$, $A = \frac{1}{2}A_0$ or $N = \frac{1}{2}N_0$

$$\therefore \frac{1}{2}A_0 = A_0e^{-\lambda T_{1/2}} \quad \frac{1}{2}N_0 = N_0e^{-\lambda T_{1/2}}$$

$$\therefore \frac{1}{2} = e^{-\lambda T_{1/2}}$$

$$\therefore -\lambda T_{1/2} = \ln\frac{1}{2} = -0.693$$

$$\therefore T_{1/2} = \frac{0.693}{\lambda} \quad (3.4)$$

The half-life of a radionuclide is thus a constant describing how fast the material is disintegrating. A short half-life indicates rapid decay with a large decay constant. Its value may be found experimentally by monitoring the activity of the sample over a period of time.

Since
$$A = A_0e^{-\lambda t}$$
$$\therefore \ln A = \ln A_0 - \lambda t$$

and a plot of $\ln A$ against t yields a straight line of gradient $-\lambda$. $T_{1/2}$ can then be found from λ using

$$T_{1/2} = \frac{0.693}{\lambda}$$

Specific activity

Non-radioactive isotopes of an element behave *chemically* the same as the radioisotopes of that element. If they are present in a sample they are referred to as **carriers**. If no such carriers are present, then the sample is described as being carrier-free.

An important term in the preparation of a sample is its **specific activity**, which depends on the relative proportion of carriers present. It is defined as the activity divided by the total mass of the element present, $\frac{A}{m}$ and is measured in Bq kg^{-1}.

A sample with very few carriers thus has a high specific activity.

Half-life – Worked example

A radioactive sample has an initial activity of 6.0 MBq and a half-life of 25 s. Calculate its activity after 2 minutes.

From equation 3.4,

$$\lambda = \frac{0.693}{T_{1/2}} = \frac{0.693}{25\,\text{s}} = 0.0277\,\text{s}^{-1}$$

Using equation 3.3,

$$A = A_0e^{-\lambda t}$$

and substituting $A_0 = 6\,\text{MBq}$, $t = 2 \times 60 = 120\,\text{s}$ and $\lambda = 0.0277\,\text{s}^{-1}$
$$A = 6\,\text{MBq}\,e^{-0.0277 \times 120}$$
$$\therefore A = 0.22\,\text{MBq} \quad (2\text{sf})$$

The activity after 2 minutes is thus 0.22 MBq.

Table 3.1 lists some common radionuclides with their half-lives, and illustrates that the naturally-occurring radionuclides in evidence today have very long half-lives.

Physical, biological and effective half-life

Once a radionuclide has been administered to a patient, it is removed from the body by biological processes such as respiration, urination and defecation. This is described by a biological decay constant λ_b.

The overall (or effective) decay constant λ_e is thus greater than the radioactive decay constant λ_r alone, as the radionuclide is being removed by both processes simultaneously, i.e.

$$\lambda_e = \lambda_r + \lambda_b$$

This means that the **effective half-life** T_e is less than the **physical half-life** T_r due to radioactive decay alone. T_e is the average time taken for half the radioactive material to be removed from the body by both processes together. It is also possible to define a **biological half-life** T_b as the time taken for biological processes to remove half the available material, assuming that no new material is arriving.

From equation 3.4,

$$\lambda = \frac{0.693}{T_{1/2}}$$

Hence, using the equation above

$$\frac{0.693}{T_e} = \frac{0.693}{T_r} + \frac{0.693}{T_b}$$

$$\therefore \frac{1}{T_e} = \frac{1}{T_r} + \frac{1}{T_b} \qquad (3.5)$$

The biological half-life of a given substance, reflecting its metabolic turnover, tends to vary from one individual to another and from one organ to another. It also depends on diet, exercise and disease. Accurate estimates of the biological (and hence effective) half-life are thus difficult to make and can cause serious problems regarding dosage assessments. The best estimations are obtained from sequential imaging studies, or multiple blood/urine sampling.

Effective half-life – Worked example

The human serum albumin labelled with ^{125}I is sometimes administered during radioactive tracer investigations. ^{125}I has a physical half-life of 60 days, but is biologically cleared from the body with a half-life of 21 days. Estimate the effective half-life.

This is calculated using equation 3.5:

$$\frac{1}{T_e} = \frac{1}{60} + \frac{1}{21} \ \ \text{days}^{-1}$$

where T_e is the effective half-life in days.

$$\therefore T_e = 16 \text{ days} \qquad (2\text{sf})$$

Thus, half of the administered radionuclide will be removed from the body in about 16 days.

Table 3.1 The half-lives of various radionuclides.

Radioisotope	Element	Half-life $T_{1/2}$
Natural		
^{3}H (tritium)	hydrogen	12–26 years
^{14}C	carbon	5760 years
^{226}Ra	radium	1600 years
^{238}U	uranium	4.5×10^9 years
Artificial		
^{15}O	oxygen	2 minutes
^{24}Na	sodium	15 hours
^{60}Co	cobalt	5.3 years
^{99m}Tc	technetium	6 hours
^{123}I	iodine	13 hours
^{131}I	iodine	8 days

RADIOACTIVE DECAY

- Useful terms include
  Mass number A = number of **neutrons** + **protons** in a nucleus.
  Atomic number Z = number of **protons** in a nucleus.
  Nuclide = species of nucleus, having a particular A and Z (also called an **isotope**).
  Radionuclide = unstable nuclide that spontaneously **decays** by emitting α-, β-, or γ-radiation (also called a **radioisotope**).
  The **activity A** of a sample is the number of disintegrations occurring per second.
  1 **Becquerel (Bq)** is an activity of 1 disintegration per second.
  The **half-life, $T_{1/2}$,** of the radionuclide, is the *average* time taken for half the radioactive atoms in the sample to decay.
- **Radioactive decay** is exponential.
  $$\frac{dN}{dt} = -\lambda N,$$
  where λ is the **decay constant**
  $$N = N_0 e^{-\lambda t} \quad \text{or} \quad A = A_0 e^{-\lambda t}$$
  $$T_{1/2} = \frac{0.693}{\lambda}$$
- The **effective half-life T_e** *inside* the body is $\dfrac{1}{T_e} = \dfrac{1}{T_r} + \dfrac{1}{T_b}$

EMISSION OF NUCLEAR RADIATION

Radioactive nuclei decay by the emission of α-, β- or γ-radiation.

α-emission

An alpha (α) particle is identical to a helium nucleus, consisting of two protons and two neutrons. It thus carries a charge of +2e, and has a rest mass of about 7×10^{-27} kg.

Decay by α-particle emission occurs mainly amongst nuclei of the heavier elements of atomic number greater than that of lead ($Z = 82$) and results in a reduction of 2 in atomic number (Z) and 4 in mass number (A) of the radionuclide. For example, radium decays to radon (Rn) in this way:

$$^{226}_{88}\text{Ra} \rightarrow {}^{222}_{86}\text{Rn} + {}^{4}_{2}\alpha$$

β-emission

A β-particle can either carry a negative charge of –e (the familiar electron), or an equal but opposite positive charge +e (the positron). It occurs basically through the transformation between neutrons and protons.

In β⁻-decay, a neutron transforms to a proton

$$^{1}_{0}\text{n} \rightarrow {}^{1}_{1}\text{p} + {}^{0}_{-1}\beta^{-} + \bar{\nu}$$
neutron → proton + electron + antineutrino

Radionuclides having an excess of neutrons usually decay by this mode. For example, phosphorus (P) decays to sulphur (S) in this way:

$$^{32}_{16}\text{P} \rightarrow {}^{32}_{17}\text{S} + {}^{0}_{-1}\beta^{-} + \bar{\nu}$$

The neutrino and its antiparticle, the antineutrino, are particles of zero charge and approximately zero mass which carry away a certain amount of energy and momentum from such disintegration processes.

In β⁺-decay, a proton transforms to a neutron

$$^{1}_{1}\text{p} \rightarrow {}^{1}_{0}\text{n} + {}^{0}_{1}\beta^{+} + \nu$$
proton →neutron + positron + neutrino

Neutron-deficient radionuclides often decay in this way. For example, sodium (Na) decays to neon (Ne) as follows:

$$^{22}_{11}\text{Na} \rightarrow {}^{22}_{10}\text{Ne} + {}^{0}_{1}\beta^{+} + \nu$$

In such decays, the mass number A remains the same and the atomic number Z changes by 1.

γ-ray emission and metastable states

γ-rays are high energy electromagnetic radiation. They are emitted from a nucleus during transitions from an excited nuclear state to a lower-energy nuclear state. Such γ-ray emission often follows another decay process such as α- or β-emission, which has left the new or **daughter** nucleus in an excited state. Pure γ-emission alone does not change the A or Z numbers of the nuclide.

Mostly the γ-rays are emitted within a fraction of a microsecond of the primary decay, but sometimes there is a delay if the daughter nucleus is left in a **metastable state**. This is indicated by the symbol m, as is the case with technetium-99m (^{99m}Tc), one of the most important radionuclides used in medicine.

Radioactive decay processes – Worked example

Write down the equations representing the following decay processes:
a) tellurium $^{131}_{52}\text{Te}$ decays to iodine I by β^--emission
b) the metastable technetium $^{99m}_{43}\text{Tc}$ is formed from the parent molybdenum $^{99}_{42}\text{Mo}$
c) iodine I decays with the emission of a β^--particle and a γ-photon to xenon $^{131}_{54}\text{Xe}$.

a) In β^--decay, A remains the same and Z increases by 1. Thus:

$$^{131}_{52}\text{Te} \rightarrow {}^{131}_{53}\text{I} + {}^{0}_{-1}\beta^- + \bar{\nu}$$

b) Again this must be β^--decay:

$$^{99}_{42}\text{Mo} \rightarrow {}^{99m}_{43}\text{Tc} + {}^{0}_{-1}\beta^- + \bar{\nu}$$

c) Here, the γ-decay does not change the value of A or Z. Hence:

$$^{131}_{53}\text{I} \rightarrow {}^{131}_{54}\text{Xe} + {}^{0}_{-1}\beta^- + \bar{\nu} + \gamma$$

NUCLEAR DECAY

- An **unstable** nucleus may become more stable through α-, β- or γ-decay.
- The table summarises the decay processes.

Decay process	Change in A	Change in Z
α	-4	-2
β^-	none	$+1$
β^+	none	-1
γ	none	none

- A **metastable** nucleus (indicated by m) remains in an excited state for a period of time before decaying, e.g. ^{99m}Tc.

PRODUCTION OF ARTIFICIAL RADIONUCLIDES

Hundreds of radionuclides can be produced *'artificially'* by a variety of methods, most of which strive to provide a product of as high a concentration of radioactive atoms as possible. This allows the user greater flexibility since a radionuclide can always be 'diluted' by the addition of inactive **'carriers'**.

The methods largely involve the bombardment of certain stable nuclei by high-energy particles such as neutrons, protons, deuterons and α-particles. The resulting nuclear reactions can lead to the formation of useful radionuclides.

Neutrons of sufficient energy to induce such nuclear reactions may be obtained in nuclear reactors and high-energy charged particles can be supplied from particle accelerators. The radionuclides so formed may then either be used directly, or provide the basis for generators located in the hospitals themselves.

Technetium-99m

This **metastable radionuclide** is formed from molybdenum in a β^--decay process having a half-life of 67 hours:

$$^{99}_{42}\text{Mo} \rightarrow {}^{99m}_{43}\text{Tc} + {}^{0}_{-1}\beta^- + \bar{\nu} \qquad \textbf{(67 hours)}$$

It subsequently decays by γ-emission with a half-life of 6 hours.

$$^{99m}_{43}\text{Tc} \rightarrow {}^{99}_{43}\text{Tc} + \gamma \qquad \textbf{(6 hours)}$$

These are the γ-rays that are so useful in radioactive tracer studies. Thereafter, $^{99}_{43}\text{Tc}$ has a half-life of about a quarter of a million years, and would therefore be classified as relatively 'stable'!

The technetium generator

Technetium's relatively short half-life (6 hours) demands that it is produced where it is to be used, i.e. in the hospital, and so a generator system is employed (figure 3.3).

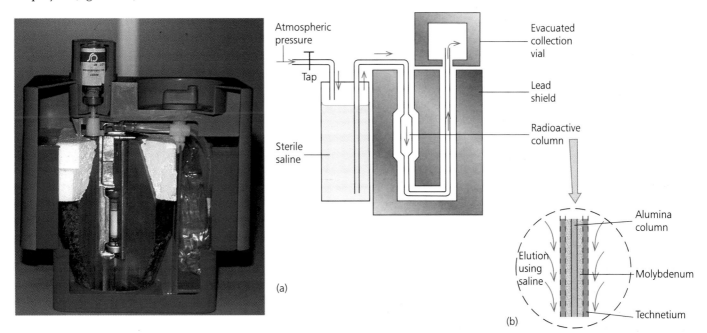

(a)

(b)

Figure 3.3 (a) A typical technetium generator used in hospitals to generate ^{99m}Tc. The entire generator is surrounded by a lead shield to absorb not only the γ-rays from the decaying technetium, but also the β⁻-radiation produced during the decay of molybdenum. **(b)** Eluting the generator to remove the technetium.

Inside a glass tube housing is a small alumina column, onto which is absorbed ^{99}**Mo** (the **parent**). This continuously decays, from an initial activity of about 10 GBq, to the **daughter** ^{99m}Tc. When required, the ^{99m}Tc is obtained by flushing the parent with a saline solution, a process known as **elution**. This is achieved by piercing an evacuated glass collecting vial onto a needle at the top of the generator. Atmospheric pressure then forces saline through the system into the vial, washing the technetium with it.

The molybdenum is chemically attached to the column and so is not removed during elution, although regular checks are necessary to ensure that there are no traces of molybdenum (or aluminium from the column) in the eluted samples. The concentrated technetium in saline is then ready to be diluted and attached to a suitable compound for administering to the body (figure 3.4).

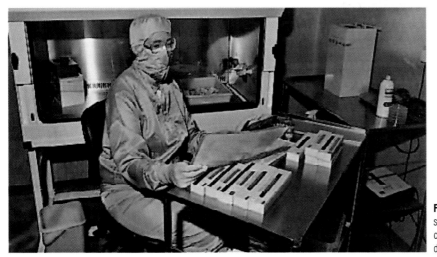

Figure 3.4 The preparation of labelled compounds for tracer studies is a skillful task, performed each morning under very carefully controlled conditions, in the hospital nuclear medicine department, ready for the day's examinations.

The technetium generator, or '**cow**', is usually 'milked' daily, leaving sufficient time in between for the technetium to build up again (figure 3.5). It needs replacing approximately weekly, because the molybdenum activity falls to an inadequate level after this time. The molybdenum itself is produced either in a reactor or a particle accelerator.

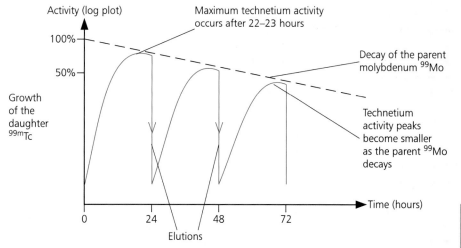

Figure 3.5 Activities in the technetium generator.

The nuclear reactor

A fission reactor operating on natural uranium consists of a lattice of uranium rods (^{235}U) embedded in a so-called moderating material. When the uranium fuel rods are irradiated with neutrons, the ^{235}U atoms capture neutrons to form the unstable ^{236}U, which then splits into two heavy fragments of approximately equal size during a process known as **fission**. For example:

$$^{235}_{92}U + ^{1}_{0}n \rightarrow ^{236}_{92}U \rightarrow ^{138}_{53}I + ^{95}_{39}Y + 3^{1}_{0}n + energy$$

A large number of useful radionuclides are formed as fission products and can be chemically separated from the used uranium fuel rods of the reactor to yield relatively carrier-free radionuclides of high specific activities (e.g. strontium, iodine and caesium). However, separation costs can be high due to the problems encountered through radiation hazards.

The fast neutrons produced simultaneously with the fission fragments are slowed down in the surrounding moderator, which is commonly carbon (graphite). Some of the resulting slow (or 'thermal') neutrons are then captured by more ^{235}U nuclei and a chain reaction commences. The rest can be utilised to irradiate stable targets placed in the reactor and so produce radionuclides.

Transient radioactive equilibrium

The rate of radioactive decay depends on the number of radioactive atoms present

$$\frac{dN}{dt} = -\lambda N$$

After an elution, there are very *few technetium* nuclei present, but *many molybdenum* nuclei available to produce it by their decay. Thus, initially, the rate of production of technetium exceeds the rate at which it decays. As the amount of technetium increases, its activity increases and eventually (after about 23 hours) a situation is reached in which the rate of production of technetium is *equal* to its rate of decay. A state of **transient equilibrium** is reached.

Thereafter, since technetium has a shorter half-life than molybdenum, the technetium decays at a faster rate than it is produced. Both parent and daughter decay together, making the 24-hourly removal of the technetium ideal.

Nuclear reactor production methods

A radionuclide can be produced artificially by bombarding a stable nucleus with high-energy particles such as neutrons. These particles are particularly advantageous since their lack of charge enables them to penetrate target nuclei without experiencing any Coulomb repulsion. Furthermore, they are in plentiful supply in a **nuclear reactor**.

Using a remote handling device, a sample of pure nuclide is placed inside the reactor, where it is irradiated by neutrons. Although a number of possible reactions can occur, the most common one is **neutron capture**, in which a slow neutron is absorbed by a nucleus and a γ-ray is emitted.

In such an (n,γ) reaction, the Z of the target atom remains unchanged but its A increases by 1. For example, the cobalt reaction proceeds as follows:

$$^{59}_{27}\text{Co} + ^{1}_{0}\text{n} \rightarrow ^{60}_{27}\text{Co} + \gamma$$

which may be abbreviated to:

$$^{59}_{27}\text{Co (n,\gamma)} \, ^{60}_{27}\text{Co}$$

Thus, the product radionuclide is chemically identical with the target, making separation by chemical means impossible. Since only a small fraction of the target atoms undergoes neutron capture, the radionuclide sample so produced contains a large percentage of carriers.

Sometimes however, the product itself subsequently decays (often by β⁻-emission, since it is now neutron-rich) to yield a further radionuclide. This is then chemically different from the target, from which it can easily be separated. For instance, the medically important ^{131}I (iodine) is produced from neutron-irradiated Te (tellurium) in this way.

Production of ^{131}I

The radionuclide ^{131}**I (iodine)** has been used in investigations of the **thyroid** (a gland in the neck responsible for producing certain hormones) (figure 3.6). Its half-life is 8 days and it decays by the emission of β⁻- and γ-rays.

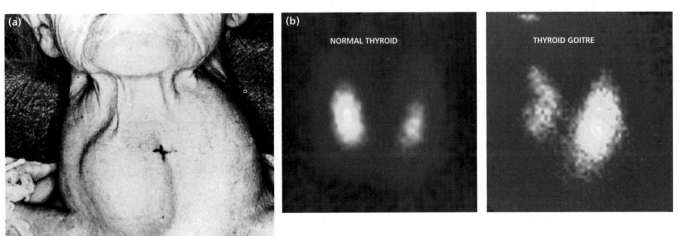

Figure 3.6 (a) A goitre (enlargement of the thyroid gland). Such an extreme case is not often seen now. **(b)** Scans showing a normal and enlarged thyroid.

It is produced by bombarding tellurium with slow (thermal) neutrons in a nuclear fission reactor.

$$^{130}_{52}\text{Te} + ^{1}_{0}\text{n} \rightarrow ^{131}_{52}\text{Te} + \gamma$$

Further spontaneous decay then yields iodine:

$$^{131}_{52}\text{Te} \rightarrow ^{131}_{53}\text{I} + ^{0}_{-1}\beta + \bar{v}$$

The irradiated tellurium target remains in the reactor for up to a month, after which time it is removed and the iodine is separated from the tellurium by standard chemical means. Special procedures, however, are necessary in these separation processes, since the materials involved are highly radioactive and often in small quantities.

RADIOPHARMACEUTICALS

The radionuclide suitable for a particular study needs to be chemically incorporated into another compound to carry it to the desired body location. The **labelled compound** so formed is called a **radiopharmaceutical**.

The process of preparing these radiopharmaceuticals is a complex one, requiring skill, care and caution. The final product must be sterile (germ-free), non-toxic, of precisely known chemical composition, compatible with the body and behave just like the substance being investigated, so that it accurately reflects body behaviour.

The radionuclide must have certain properties. It should

- emit *only* γ-radiation, since α- and β-radiations are readily absorbed in the body, causing damage through ionisation and difficulty with detection
- have a *conveniently* short half-life, short enough to avoid excessive radiation damage, yet long enough to allow detection
- emit γ- radiation of an energy suitable for easy detection by a gamma camera
- be readily and cheaply available, at high concentrations
- be easily attached to convenient compounds to transport it to the targeted destination.

By far the most popular radionuclide used in diagnostic studies is ^{99m}Tc. Indeed, it accounts for 90% of radionuclide imaging, and a whole branch of 'technetium chemistry' has developed, to investigate new ways of attaching technetium to useful pharmaceuticals.

In the past, ^{131}I was also an important radionuclide, used in thyroid investigations. It does, however, suffer from several major disadvantages. Firstly, it emits β-radiation, leading to larger radiation doses. Secondly, its 364 keV γ-rays are of too high an energy for good image quality in the gamma camera. Finally, its 8-day half-life is too long, leading to high doses and restricting the permissible administered activities.

RADIOACTIVE TRACERS

- Radionuclides are produced by elution methods, e.g. ^{99m}Tc in the **technetium generator** in the hospital.
  ^{99m}Tc is formed from the decay of molybdenum
  $$^{99}_{42}\text{Mo} \rightarrow ^{99m}_{43}\text{Tc} + ^{0}_{-1}\beta^- + \bar{v},$$
  ($T_{1/2} = 67$ h).
- **Nuclear reactor** methods are also used to produce radionuclides, e.g. ^{131}I production:
  tellurium-130 is bombarded by neutrons
  $$^{130}_{52}\text{Te} + ^{1}_{0}\text{n} \rightarrow ^{131}_{52}\text{Te} + \gamma$$
  further spontaneous decay yields iodine
  $$^{131}_{52}\text{Te} \rightarrow ^{131}_{53}\text{I} + ^{0}_{-1}\beta^- + \bar{v}$$
- A radionuclide is 'attached' to a suitable chemical compound to form a **tracer**.
- The most common medical radionuclide is ^{99m}Tc, which has a convenient **half-life** of 6 hours, emits only γ-rays, its γ-energy is ideal for **gamma camera** detection, is easily attached to suitable chemical compounds to form **tracers**.

These difficulties are now overcome by using the isotope ^{123}I, which emits only γ-rays, with a shorter half-life of 13.2 hours (table 3.3). It is, however, more expensive!

Table 3.3 Advantages of ^{99m}Tc and ^{123}I in diagnostic studies.

^{99m}Tc	^{123}I
convenient half-life of 6 hours	convenient half-life of 13 hours for uptake tests
emits only γ-rays (safer for patient)	emits only γ-rays
γ-rays emitted are of a convenient energy (140 keV) for the gamma camera	γ-rays emitted are of a convenient energy (159 keV) for the gamma camera (although some higher energies, around 500–600 keV, are also emitted and can reduce image quality slightly)
easily attached to different compounds to form radioactive tracers	concentrates in the thyroid, allowing easy investigation
easily produced in hospitals using a generator	readily available using accelerator methods

Due to the large world wide demand for labelled compounds, many compounds are mass-produced and freeze-dried. They can then be reconstituted as required and mixed with the relevant radioisotope, as part of the hospital's daily radiopharmaceutical preparations (see figure 3.4). The storage, handling and waste disposal of such materials are subject to strict controls (see page 113).

RADIONUCLIDE IMAGING

Although radionuclides have been used in therapy since the early 1930s, their *diagnostic* potential was not appreciated for another 30 years. The so-called **nuclear imaging** techniques did not gain immediate popularity, as the images obtained were indistinct, compared with those obtained using X-rays.

It was gradually appreciated, however, that **nuclear medicine** had a unique strength, namely its ability to study body *function* rather than *structure*. Furthermore, the clarity of image has steadily improved with gamma camera technology (figure 3.7), so that radioisotope imaging has now developed into a strong, *complementary* imaging modality, alongside X-rays, ultrasound and nuclear magnetic resonance.

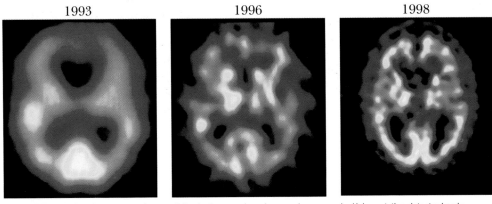

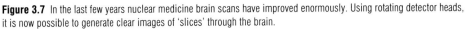

Figure 3.7 In the last few years nuclear medicine brain scans have improved enormously. Using rotating detector heads, it is now possible to generate clear images of 'slices' through the brain.

Radioactive tracer studies

If a radionuclide or a labelled compound is introduced into the body, its passage through the body can be 'traced' through the radiation it emits. For this reason, it is known simply as a **radioactive tracer**. The amount of tracer introduced must be small, so that the system under investigation is not changed, and this demands samples of high concentration. Sample activities of around 500 MBq are common, being carried by masses of radionuclide of the order of nanograms.

In **static imaging**, after a suitable time interval, maybe a few hours, a scan of the body is made to monitor the concentration of the radionuclide in specific organs, using a **gamma camera** (figure 3.8).

In **dynamic imaging**, a series of images is taken over a period of time, starting at or just before the injection of the tracer, again using a gamma camera. These images demonstrate both the distribution and the amount taken up or excreted by the various organs. A dynamic heart or lung investigation may span a few minutes, whereas a kidney or bladder study takes nearer half-an-hour (figure 3.9).

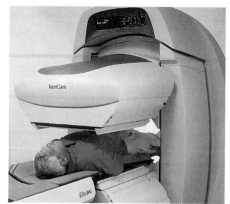

Figure 3.8 A modern compact gamma camera is at the heart of this whole body scanner, used for detecting the spread of cancer through the body.

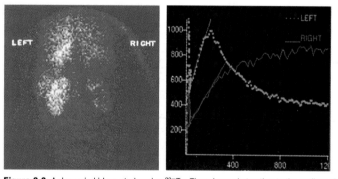

Figure 3.9 A dynamic kidney study using ^{99m}Tc. There is an obstruction to the outflow of urine from the patient's right kidney, (possibly due to pressure from an adjacent enlarged prostate gland, or a stone, blood clot or tumour restricting the outflow). You can see the retarded function of the right kidney from both the images and the graphs. If untreated, this condition often leads to kidney failure.

The resulting images are then analysed. Local **hot spots**, indicating higher than normal tracer concentration, and **cold spots**, showing a lack of tracer, are often indicative of disease (see figure 3.6). Computer-assisted processing can quickly and easily compute the percentage uptake of a relevant organ and compare it with normal values (or even compare pairs of organs, like the lungs or kidneys), allowing diagnosis and treatment recommendations.

The gamma camera

The gamma camera (figure 3.10) is used to produce an image of the body, based on the γ-rays coming from radionuclides inside the body. It consists essentially of the

- **collimator**, to define the incident beam direction
- **scintillator**, to convert the incoming γ-rays into visible light flashes
- array of **photomultiplier tubes (PMTs)** to transform the flashes into amplified electrical pulses
- associated **circuitry**, to analyse and process the electrical information and form an image.

Each initial γ-ray is eventually transformed into a single dot on a final image, which is then built up from hundreds of thousands of such signals.

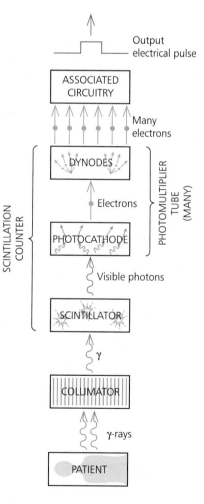

Figure 3.10 Block diagram of the gamma camera.

The collimator

This acts rather like the grid used in X-ray imaging. Its purpose is to define exactly where in the patient the γ-ray originated. It consists of a lead disc, normally 2–4 cm thick, in which are drilled tens of thousands of holes, parallel to the axis of the disc. Only γ-rays striking the collimator perpendicular to it will pass through, thus clearly defining their incident direction. All non-axial rays are absorbed in the lead (figure 3.11).

The thickness of the collimator is carefully chosen to match the relevant γ-ray energy. It is just thick enough to stop non-axial rays penetrating, but not too thick to reduce sensitivity unnecessarily.

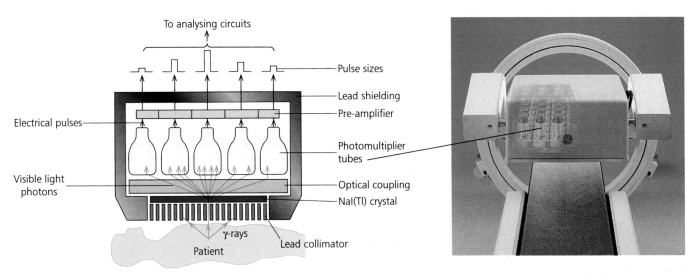

Figure 3.11 The gamma camera head.

Collimation

Since the collimator is removing a great deal of the incident radiation, it inherently reduces the **sensitivity** of the detector to radiation (typically by a factor of as much as 10 000). However, it improves the **spatial resolution** by increasing the precision with which the source of γ-rays is located, which in turn gives improved definition in the final image.

Varying the size and number of holes in the collimator provides a flexible 'trade-off' between sensitivity and resolution, and a range of removable collimators is available for different applications (figure 3.12). A larger number of smaller holes (e.g. 80 000 holes of 1 mm diameter) favours better resolution (typically 3 mm), but lower sensitivity.

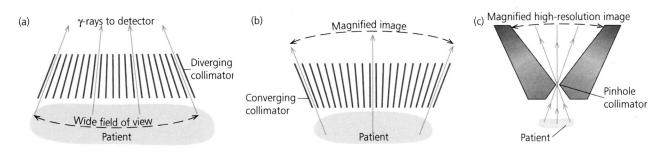

Figure 3.12 Various shapes of collimator are available for specific studies: **(a)** the diverging collimator increases the effective field of view for large area scans (e.g. the lungs) whilst the converging version **(b)** provides magnification of a restricted region (imaging children). The pin-hole collimator **(c)** gives a magnified, high-resolution image of small organs (e.g. the thyroid).

The scintillator

When X- or γ-radiation is absorbed in certain materials, known as **phosphors** or **scintillators**, their atoms are raised to excited states. They subsequently return to their ground states by the emission of *visible photons*. These minute flashes of light in the phosphor, called **scintillations**, thus provide a means of detecting γ-rays. The most common phosphor is a **sodium iodide crystal** (see box).

As the scintillations are too small to be detected directly, they need amplification using a PMT. An array of such tubes behind the phosphor is used to detect, locate and amplify the initial scintillation.

Sodium iodide as a scintillator

In the gamma camera, the scintillator is a large sodium iodide crystal, activated with about 0.5% of thallium oxide, abbreviated to NaI(Tl). It offers several advantages:

- the relatively large atomic number of iodine (53) and the high crystal density make it an excellent γ-ray absorber (about 90% of ^{99m}Tc gamma rays are absorbed in a crystal thickness of about 1 cm)
- each gamma photon absorbed produces a flash of light, containing about 5000 light photons. This is efficient energy conversion

- the flash (or scintillation) lasts less than a microsecond, permitting high count rates (up to about $10^4 s^{-1}$).

Disadvantages are that NaI is easily damaged by temperature changes and is hygroscopic (absorbs water), so the crystals must be kept hermetically sealed. They are usually purchased in sealed aluminium cans, having a glass or quartz window on the side to be in contact with the PMTs. Transparent silicone grease is usually employed to provide good optical contact with the face of the PMTs.

The photomultipier tubes (PMTs)

Light photons from the scintillator fall on the light-sensitive cathode, or **photocathode**, of the PMTs thereby ejecting **photoelectrons** by the photoelectric effect.

These photoelectrons are then accelerated towards the first of a series of electrodes or **dynodes** that are held at increasing positive potentials along the tube (figure 3.13). Each electron incident on its surface easily ejects from it a few secondary electrons. These in turn are accelerated to the next dynode where further secondary electrons are ejected, and so on down the chain of normally ten dynodes until the final anode is reached. If there is an average multiplication of four at each of the ten dynodes, every primary photoelectron will result in a pulse of 4^{10} (about a million) secondary electrons at the anode. Such a large overall gain enables even low-energy radiations to be detected and measured.

Materials

The **photocathode** is a thin layer of semiconductor material (often antimony-caesium) to yield high photoelectric conversion efficiency (10–25%).

The **dynodes** require low work functions to give high amplification. (The work function of a material is the minimum amount of energy that must be supplied to an electron to liberate it from the surface.) A beryllium-copper alloy is a popular choice.

The **PMTs** demand special shielding (e.g. mu-metal) to prevent stray radiation activating the sensitive dynodes, and creating a 'dark current'.

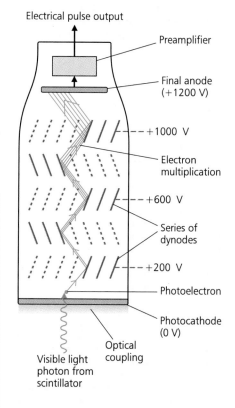

Figure 3.13 The photomultiplier tube.

An important feature of the PMT is that the size of the **output electrical pulse** is *directly proportional* to the incoming visible photon energy, since each pulse of light is amplified by the same factor. For example, if four visible photons fall on the photocathode, the output pulse will be four times as large as that due to one visible photon arriving. This provides a means of identifying where in the patient the original γ-ray originated, since the largest signal will come from the PMT closest to the scintillation, which in turn is in line with the source of the γ-ray (see figure 3.11). An array of up to 75 PMTs is located behind a single sodium iodide crystal (figure 3.14) and, from the output pulses, electronic analysis can easily identify the location of the incoming γ-ray.

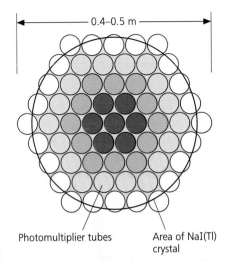

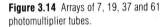

Figure 3.14 Arrays of 7, 19, 37 and 61 photomultiplier tubes.

Maximum count rates

The ability of the gamma camera to record high count rates is limited more by the performance of the PMTs than by the NaI(Tl) crystal. The output of the PMT is an electrical pulse of a fraction of a microsecond duration, but this time is increased further during amplification. If another γ-ray arrives during this time it will not be recorded. This '**dead time**' of the detector is typically 0.5 μs, giving maximum count rates of 200 000 counts per second. This is important in dynamic studies.

The scintillation counter

The combination of scintillating crystal and single photomultiplier tube is called a **scintillation counter**. It simply counts the number of incoming γ- (or X-) ray photons, rather than giving information about their origin. Only by using an array of such scintillation counters, as in the gamma camera, can an actual image be formed.

The associated circuitry

The **position decoding circuit** (figure 3.15) compares all the PMT pulse values and ascribes an *x–y* location to the incoming γ-ray. This, however, is not enough. We need to establish that the incoming γ-ray actually came from the scanned radioisotope and not from some other source, or from heavily scattered lower energy radiation.

To do this, the *total γ-ray energy* deposited in the phosphor is estimated by summing all the PMT pulses in an **addition circuit**. This signal is then fed to a **pulse-height analyser**, which only gives an output (the 'Z' or brightness pulse) if the γ-energy falls within certain predetermined limits, or '**energy window**'. If this is the case, the oscilloscope beam is 'switched on' and a dot is produced on the screen at the appropriate *x–y* location.

The recording is continued until the desired number of counts (dots) has been obtained (typically 300 000–500 000 for small fields of view and up to a million for larger fields of view). The oscilloscope dot picture may then be photographed using a camera with a long exposure time, or stored in digital form in the memory of a computer.

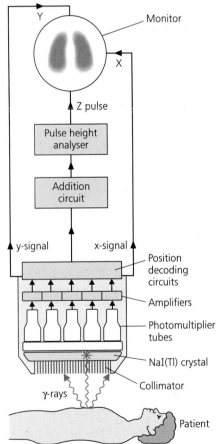

Figure 3.15 Gamma camera imaging system.

Image quality

The gamma camera only works well within a relatively narrow range of γ-energy. If the energy is too high, a large percentage of the incident γ-rays pass straight through the phosphor without detection. On the other hand, if the energy is too low, more γ-photons are absorbed in the patient, reducing image quality and increasing patient dose.

A particular camera will thus be designed for use with a specified radiation, such as the 140 keV ^{99m}Tc emission, employing the most appropriate collimator and crystal. The energy window on the pulse-height analyser is typically set at 20%, thus accepting photons (of ±10% the optimum energy) that have undergone some scatter. For example, in ^{99m}Tc monitoring, γ-rays with energies from 126–154 keV would be counted. Any further increase in window leads to poorer image quality, although it can decrease imaging time.

Image quality can be improved by increasing the number of dots creating it. This involves either

- administering a higher activity tracer to the patient, with obvious dose disadvantages, or
- increasing the imaging time, with associated problems of patient movement blur.

A typical scan will take between 100 and 200 s, acquire up to a million counts and give a spatial resolution of about 3 mm. The **brightness** of the final image at any point reflects the **corresponding γ-ray activity** at that point in the patient.

Although the development of digital imaging techniques has greatly improved image quality, the final resolution obtainable is still limited by the size and number of PMTs used. Further advances using solid-state detector-based cameras hold great prospects for the future, as also do the other radionuclide imaging techniques, discussed on the Web page.

RADIONUCLIDE APPLICATIONS

These can broadly be divided into **localisation** (or **uptake**) **tests**, assessing function, and **dilution analysis** to measure body composition.

Uptake tests

In order to investigate a body organ, a suitable radioactive tracer, having a particular affinity for that organ, is selected and administered to the body. The uptake of the tracer by the organ of interest is then assessed by imaging with the gamma camera. The results can then be displayed qualitatively as an image (see figure 3.6) or quantitatively as a graphical analysis (figure 3.16). Table 3.4 summarises some of the more common imaging applications.

RADIONUCLIDE IMAGING

- Displays **body function**.
- The **gamma camera** maps γ-rays from radioactive tracers in the body.
- A lead **collimator** defines where the radiation is coming from.
- A **scintillating crystal**, NaI(Tl), converts the incoming γ-radiation into visible radiation (**scintillations**).
- An array of **photomultiplier tubes** transforms the visible radiation into amplified electrical pulses.
- **Electronic circuits** analyse and display the data as a final image.
- **Image quality** may be improved by:
  imaging over a **narrow energy range**, using **fine collimators**, giving the patient **higher-activity tracers**, increasing the number of **photomultiplier tubes**.

Table 3.4 Radionuclides used in medical imaging.

Organ	Tracers	Investigations
Uptake tests		
bone	^{99m}Tc	bone metabolism and localisation of bone disease, e.g. cancer
	^{45}Ca	calcium absorption studies
thyroid	^{123}I	evaluation of gland size
	^{99m}Tc	assessment of thyroid function
	(^{131}I)	(treatment of thyroid cancer)
liver	^{99m}Tc	liver disease and disorders of its blood supply studied using colloidal suspension
heart and circulation	^{99m}Tc	labelled red blood cells used to monitor cardiac output, blood volume and circulation
		blood clots (thrombosis) identified through build-up of tracer at that point
	^{201}Tl	heart muscle function investigated
lungs	^{133}Xe	aerosols labelled with ^{133}Xe or ^{99m}Tc used for ventilation studies,
	^{99m}Tc	^{99m}Tc used for monitoring blood flow
kidneys and bladder	^{99m}Tc	blood and urine flow assessed
brain	^{99m}Tc	brain blood flow and function
	^{123}I	dementia diagnosed, stroke damage assessed
	(^{15}O,^{18}F)	brain receptors and response to drugs monitored using PET studies. See Web page.
tumours	^{18}F, ^{67}Ga, ^{111}In,	special radionuclides required to localise
	^{123}I, ^{201}Tl	tumours in particular regions
Dilution analysis		
blood	^{125}I, ^{99m}Tc	labelled human serum albumen used to estimate total body plasma and blood count
red blood cells	^{51}Cr	attached to red blood cells to assess red cell volume
water	^{3}H	tritiated water used to find total body water
sodium and potassium	^{24}Na, ^{42}K	body minerals investigated

The thyroid

The thyroid gland in the neck uses iodine to manufacture hormones. Its functioning may be investigated using thyroid uptake tests that involve the measurement of the accumulation of radioiodine (usually ^{123}I) by the thyroid gland.

Since iodine is readily absorbed from the gastrointestinal tract into the bloodstream, the patient is usually given a drink of a dilute sodium iodide solution, containing about 1 MBq of tracer, although sometimes it is injected directly into the bloodstream. The activity from the thyroid is measured using a small gamma camera with a pinhole collimator.

In quantitative studies, the thyroid count rate is compared with that from a standard or model neck (sometimes called a '**phantom**') containing the same amount of radioiodine as in the administered dose and having a volume comparable to that of an average thyroid gland (approximately $3 \times 10^{-5}\,\mathrm{m}^3$). The percentage uptake, given by:

$$\frac{\textbf{count rate from thyroid}}{\textbf{count rate from standard}} \times \textbf{100\%}$$

is evaluated after specified time periods, from 10 minutes to 48 hours. Typical values for the 24-hour test are indicated on figure 3.16, and clearly indicate either over- or under-activity.

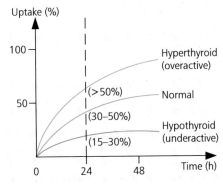

Figure 3.16 Uptake of radioiodine by the thyroid.

Careful shielding is, of course, necessary to prevent counts from the radioiodine in other parts of the body, and also from background radiation, although corrections can be made for the latter.

Other conditions that can be diagnosed from the gamma camera images are **tumours**, recognised from 'cold spots', where there is a lack of uptake of the tracer, and **goitres** (enlargement of the thyroid) (see figure 3.6 on page 57).

Since it only emits γ-radiation ^{123}I (with a half-life of 13 hours) is now preferred to ^{131}I, which emits β-radiation as well as γ-radiation. In fact, the most common radioisotope currently used in thyroid investigations is not an isotope of iodine at all! It is the familiar ^{99m}Tc, which is taken up in the same way as iodine but more easily released.

Bone studies

The preferred radioisotope for studies of bone metabolism and the localisation of bone disease is now ^{99m}Tc, incorporated into polyphosphate molecules. Following injection, the tracer is rapidly localised within the skeleton, with typically 80–90% being deposited in bone within one hour.

Any abnormalities in the bone tend to lead to an increased blood supply there. When the bone-seeking tracer is administered, the diseased areas will therefore show larger uptakes and appear as 'hot spots' on the resulting image (figure 3.17).

Such studies can often detect bone tumours, fractures (particularly **stress fractures**, the microfractures commonly developed by athletes and dancers) infections and arthritis before these become evident using a standard X-ray, since tracer studies are recording *function*, rather than *structure* (see figure 3.1).

Lung imaging

Two types of investigation are frequently employed, namely a **perfusion** (blood flow) study and a **ventilation** (air flow) study.

The tracer used in the perfusion examination is ^{99m}Tc attached to albumen, which is a component of the blood. It is injected into the bloodstream through a vein in the arm and the rather large particles become trapped in the fine capillaries of the lungs. Activity will thus be recorded from those areas receiving blood, but not from those vessels deprived of blood. Any blockages in the blood vessels, for example due to a clot, can thus be identified through 'cold spots' on the image (figure 3.18).

In ventilation studies, the patient breathes an aerosol for two minutes or so. This aerosol contains a compound labelled with ^{99m}Tc. (An alternative tracer sometimes employed is the gas ^{133}Xe, xenon.) Several gamma camera scans are immediately gathered from different aspects, the total examination lasting about half-an-hour. Any blockages in the airway can again be identified through 'cold spots' on the image.

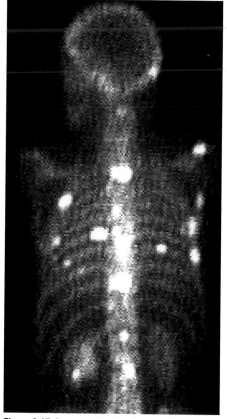

Figure 3.17 Bone scan showing widespread bone cancer, with increased tracer uptake at 'hot spots'.

Figure 3.18 Lung studies: **(a)** a normal lung scan, perfusion study left, ventilation study right; **(b)** a lung with a blood clot restricting blood flow (perfusion) in the lower right sector (arrows). The ventilation results are still normal since the airway is not blocked.

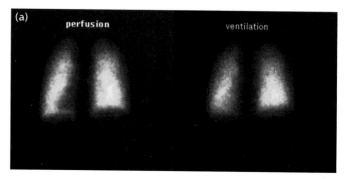

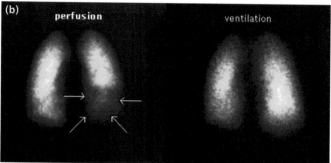

The heart

Radiocardiography (RCG) is the technique of monitoring a radioactive tracer as it flows through the heart chambers, and the resulting tracer concentration curve is referred to as a **radiocardiogram** (figure 3.19). Cardiac output and the efficiency of the heart to act as a pump to force blood around the body can then be assessed.

A popular tracer for cardiac studies is ^{99m}Tc-labelled human serum albumen. A well-collimated scintillation counter is used to detect activity.

The performance of heart muscle can also be investigated, for example to assess the extent of the damage caused after a heart attack, or to monitor the effects of exercise or drugs. A popular radioisotope here is 201-thallium (^{201}Tl) since it mimics potassium, which is utilised by muscle cells as part of their metabolic process. The patient is given an injection of radioactive thallium chloride, which is then taken up by the heart muscle cells in proportion to their blood supply. The resulting image data then gives a 'map' of blood flow, which in turn indicates the state of health of the muscles in various parts of the heart (figure 3.20).

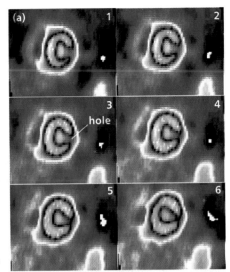

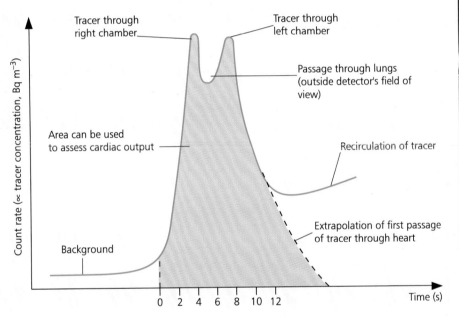

Figure 3.19 A radiocardiogram using ^{99m}Tc.

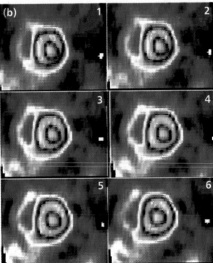

Figure 3.20 Performance of heart muscle using thallium-201. **(a)** The patient is given the tracer whilst exercising on a bicycle. Rotating gamma camera heads yield images of successive 'slices' through a chamber of the heart. These reveal a hole in the 'doughnut' shaped muscle, indicating a lack of blood to this part of the muscle, possibly caused by a blockage. **(b)** The patient is scanned again later while resting. The hole has filled in, showing that the muscle is still alive. Clearing the offending blockage should therefore lead to a full recovery.

The kidneys

The speed at which kidneys process blood and eject waste liquid (i.e. urine) to the bladder can be measured (see figure 3.9 on page 60) and blockages such as stones, identified.

Brain studies

Once again, technetium-99m is used to assess blood flow in the brain. A series of transverse 'slices', starting at the bottom of the brain and moving upwards, are usually imaged, and the blood flow colour-coded (figure 3.21). Both dementia (a loss in brain activity in old age) and stroke damage (resulting from an interrupted blood supply to the brain) show clearly identifiable patterns.

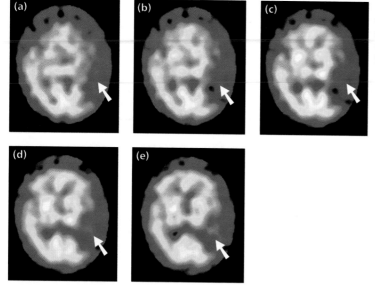

Figure 3.21 Transverse 'slices' through the brain are visualised using rotating gamma camera heads to collect multiple sets of data. These are analysed using a 'back projection' technique, like that used in X-ray computed tomography (CT) (see Web page). In these images you can see a lack of activity in the region shown by the arrows, indicating stroke damage.

Dilution analysis

This type of study essentially measures the volume (or mass) of a body fluid, such as water or blood. It is useful in investigating blood disorders such as anaemia, assessing damage following a stroke, monitoring total blood volume after an accident and so on.

Quite simply, a measured quantity of radionuclide of known activity (the **tracer**) is administered to the patient and given time to mix with the fluid under investigation (the **tracee**). A sample of the tracee is then removed and its activity measured. This yields the degree of **dilution** of the original tracer and hence leads to an estimate of the fluid volume in question.

Dilution analysis

If the activity of the tracer administered is x Bq, and it completely mixes with the volume, V m^3, of the tracee, the activity concentration (activity per unit volume) produced in the mixture is:

$$C = \frac{x}{V}\,\mathrm{Bq\,m^{-3}}$$

If the tracer is added as a small volume v of solution of high activity concentration C_1, then:

$$x = C_1 v$$

and

$$V = \frac{C_1 v}{C}$$

In practice, the activity of the original tracer is too high to measure using the same instrument employed for tracee monitoring. Hence, it is common to dilute a sample of tracer giving a **dilution factor** d:

$$d = \frac{\text{diluted volume}}{\text{undiluted volume}}$$

The measured tracer activity concentration C_2 is then C_1/d (or alternatively, $C_1 = dC_2$).

$$\therefore V = \frac{dC_2 v}{C} \qquad (3.6)$$

Thus, if d, C_2, C and v can be measured, V can be estimated.

Two possible sources of error in dilution analysis are:

a the mixing of tracer and tracee may be neither immediate nor complete

b there may be some loss of tracee from the system through biological removal. A graphical analysis (tracer concentration against time) may permit suitable corrections to be made.

Blood volume measurement – Worked example

A 10 cm³ dose of albumen labelled with about 150 kBq of ^{99m}Tc is injected into a vein in a patient's arm. Another 10 cm³ of the albumen is diluted to 6000 cm³ with water, to provide a 'standard'.

After 15 minutes, a 5 cm³ blood sample is taken from the other arm and found to have an activity of 150 Bq. 5 cm³ of the standard then has an activity of 120 Bq.
a) Why is the sample taken from the **other** arm?
b) Why is the tracer diluted to form a 'standard'?
c) Estimate the volume of the patient's blood.

a) Removing a sample from the other arm excludes contamination from the injection site and ensures thorough mixing of the tracer into the bloodstream.

b) The 'neat' tracer has an activity too high for measurement using the same instrument as that used for the blood sample. To improve accuracy by using the same range of the same instrument for all measurements, the tracer is diluted to form the 'standard'.

c) Identical volumes (10 cm³) of the 'neat' tracer originally had the *same* activity (approximately 150 kBq). (At the later sampling time, this will have fallen to the *same lower* value A Bq, due to radioactive decay.)

These samples are diluted with
i) 6000 cm³ water (standard)
ii) V cm³ blood (patient), where V cm³ is the total volume of the patient's blood.

If 5 cm³ of diluted standard has an activity of 120 Bq, then the complete standard would have an activity of

$$\frac{6000 \text{ cm}^3}{5 \text{ cm}^3} \times 120 \text{ Bq} = A$$

and similarly, if 5 cm³ of the patient's blood has an activity of 150 Bq, then his entire blood would have an activity of

$$\frac{V \text{cm}^3}{5 \text{ cm}^3} \times 150 \text{ Bq} = A$$

Equating these two values for A gives

$$\frac{6000 \text{ cm}^3 \times 120 \text{ Bq}}{5 \text{ cm}^3} = \frac{V \text{cm}^3 \times 150 \text{ Bq}}{5 \text{ cm}^3}$$

$$\therefore V = 4800 \text{ cm}^3$$

Thus, the volume of the patient's blood is approximately 5 litres.

ADVANTAGES AND DISADVANTAGES OF RADIONUCLIDE IMAGING

Advantages

1 Assesses body **function** and is particularly useful in uptake tests and in monitoring **flow** rates.
2 Can identify skeletal problems, like stress fractures, **early**, due to increased activity of bone cells.
3 Monitors **behaviour** following treatment, especially drug-induced changes.
4 Can measure body **composition** using dilution analysis.
5 **Whole body scanning** is possible, for example to assess disease of the skeleton and detect tumours when their site is not known.

Disadvantages

1 Generally **poor resolution** compared with other imaging modalities.
2 **Radiation risk** due to the administered radionuclide (but often no greater than that from comparable X-ray investigations).
3 Can be **invasive**, sometimes requiring an injection into the bloodstream. (Less than 0.001% adverse reaction, compared with 4–13% for X-ray contrast injection.)
4 Disposal of **radioactive waste**, including that from patients, requires special procedures.
5 Relatively **high costs** associated with radiotracer production and administration. (This puts nuclear medicine in a cost range just below or equivalent to MRI, rather than with X-rays or ultrasound.)

See also page 3 for a full comparison of the different imaging modalities.

TRACER APPLICATIONS

- **Uptake tests** (the tracer concentrates in particular organs).
  Bone: ^{99m}Tc used to detect cancer, stress fractures and bone graft success.
  Thyroid: ^{123}I used to assess over-active and under-active thyroids, as well as thyroid tumours, cysts and goitres.
  Lungs: ^{133}Xe inhaled for ventilation studies (airways) and ^{99m}Tc administered for perfusion studies (blood flow).
  Heart: ^{201}Tl used to study muscle performance.
  Brain: ^{99m}Tc used to assess dementia and stroke damage.
- **Dilution analysis** to assess blood and water volumes (the tracer 'mixes' with certain body fluids).
  Body **blood:** ^{99m}Tc used to assess volume.
  Red cells: ^{51}Cr is attached to these.
  Minerals: ^{24}Na and ^{42}K used to monitor body sodium and potassium.

QUESTIONS

1 a Explain the following terms:
   i radionuclide
   ii stable isotope
   iii decay constant.
  b The count rate from a radionuclide falls from 800 counts per minute to 100 counts per minute in 6 hours. What is the decay constant of the nuclide?

2 a Define the activity and half-life of a sample of radionuclide. Describe briefly how its half-life can be found experimentally.
  b A sample of the radioisotope ^{15}O of oxygen, used in PET (Positron Emission Tomography) imaging of the brain, has an activity of 4.0 MBq. It has a half-life of 2 minutes.
   i Calculate its decay constant.
   ii How long will it take for the activity to fall to 1.5 MBq?

3 a A carrier-free sample of the radioisotope ^{24}Na of sodium, used for investigating body sodium, contains 10^{18} atoms. Its half-life is 15 hours. What is meant by the expression 'carrier-free'?
  b Calculate
   i the fraction of the radioisotope remaining after 2 days
   ii the activity of the sample after 2 days.

4 a Radioactive sodium for medical purposes is produced by neutron bombardment of the stable isotope $^{23}_{11}$Na. What is a suitable source of neutrons for this reaction? Write an equation for this reaction.
  b The sample thus produced contains a large percentage of stable sodium atoms, called carriers. In some circumstances, such as the decay of $^{131m}_{52}$Te to $^{131}_{53}$I, the radioisotope produced is almost carrier free. Give the equation for the $^{131m}_{52}$Te to $^{131}_{53}$I decay. Explain why a carrier-free isotope can be obtained from this decay but not from the sodium reaction.
  c The function of the lungs can be studied using a radioactive gas such as $^{133}_{54}$Xe or $^{81m}_{36}$Kr. Using the information given below, state one advantage and one disadvantage of using Xe in preference to Kr for such investigations.

	Emission products	Half-life
$^{133}_{54}$Xe	β, γ	5.3 days
$^{81m}_{36}$Kr	γ	13 seconds

(ULEAC 1993)

QUESTIONS

5 a ^{125}I has a radioactive half-life of 60 days, but a shorter biological half-life of 21 days, mainly through excretion from the kidneys. Estimate its effective half-life.

b Will this estimate be the same for all patients? Justify your answer.

6 a Thallium-208 is a beta-minus (β^-) emitter with a half-life of 3.1 minutes. It decays into an isotope of lead whose proton number is 82. Write an equation which describes its decay. The symbol for thallium is Tl and for lead is Pb.

b Explain what problems might be encountered using this isotope of thallium for radionuclide imaging, assuming that there are no problems with its chemical behaviour.

(ULEAC 1996)

7 a Explain why, for radionuclide imaging,
  i α-particle emitting radioisotopes are not used
  ii a radionuclide which emits only monochromatic γ-rays in the energy range 60–400 keV is used.

b State **two** factors (other than its emissions), which affect the choice of radionuclide for use in a particular tracer study.

8 a Give three medical examples of the use of radioactive tracers, and in each case include the reasons for the choice of tracer. Take your examples from as wide a range of applications as possible.

b ^{131}I has a half-life of 8 days, whilst ^{99m}Tc has a half-life of only 6 hours.
  i If carrier-free samples of these two radionuclides initially have the same activity, sketch a graph to show how their activities subsequently vary with time.
  ii What implications does this have for their method of production?

9 Figure 3.22 shows a simplified diagram of a typical scintillation counter.

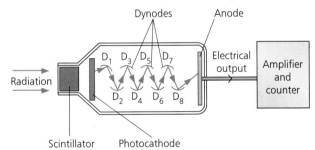

Figure 3.22

a i Explain the function of the scintillator.
  ii Suggest why a scintillator used for detecting γ-rays may not detect α-particles.
  iii Describe the function of the photocathode.

b The scintillation counter in the figure is used to detect β-particles. The anode current is 6.4×10^{-13} A. Each electron incident on a dynode results in four electrons moving on to the next dynode.
  i Calculate the number of electrons arriving at the anode in one second.
  ii There are eight dynodes in the scintillation counter. Calculate the number of electrons incident on the first dynode D_1 in one second.
  iii The rate of arrival of β-particles at the scintillator is 4000 s^{-1}. Calculate the ratio

$$\frac{\text{rate of production of electrons by the photocathode}}{\text{rate of arrival of } \beta\text{-particles at the scintillator}}$$

(Cambridge 1995)

10 Figure 3.23 shows the main components of a gamma camera.

a For each of the components labelled on the diagram, give its (A) name and (B) function in the detection of radiation.

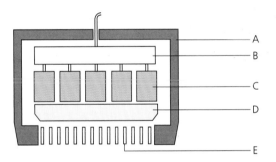

Figure 3.23

b Give **one** example of the use of a gamma camera in medical diagnosis.

c Describe the procedure which would be followed to obtain an image in the example you have given.

d How does the information obtained from such an image differ from that obtained from a diagnostic X-ray image?

(NEAB 1997)

11 a Describe a radioactive tracer study in which the tracer:
  i mixes with the substance under investigation
  ii is accumulated in the object of interest.

b A small volume of a solution which contained the sodium radioisotope ^{24}Na had an activity of 12 000 disintegrations per minute when it was injected into the bloodstream of a patient. After 30 hours, the activity of 1 cm^3 of the blood was found to be 0.5 disintegrations per minute. If ^{24}Na has a half-life of 15 hours, estimate the volume of blood in the patient. State any assumptions you make.

Magnetic resonance imaging

Although the physics of **nuclear magnetic resonance (NMR)** has been understood for half a century, its application to medical imaging did not develop until the early 1970s, through the independent work of Lauterbur and Damadian (USA) and Mansfield (Nottingham).

In 1977 the first whole-body magnetic resonance image was published and by the early 1980s, whole body scanners were available in hospitals. **Magnetic resonance imaging (MRI)** had arrived and has developed at a remarkable pace ever since.

It is easy to understand its popularity just by observing the clarity of image available (figure 4.1). What is not so easy to understand is how it works! (figure 4.2). Even the name is daunting, since it involves three very complex topics in Physics.

- *Nuclear* – the nuclei of many body atoms behave like tiny bar magnets.
- *Magnetic* – when in a strong magnetic field, these tiny 'bar magnets' align with the field, although not perfectly. They rotate, or precess, around the field direction with a particular frequency that falls in the radio frequency range.
- *Resonance* – if the body receives a short pulse of radio frequency magnetic field oscillations, those nuclei with a frequency exactly matching the incoming frequency resonate, and absorb energy. When the pulse ends, the body nuclei re-emit this energy, inducing a radio frequency signal in receiver coils outside the body. This is the MRI signal.

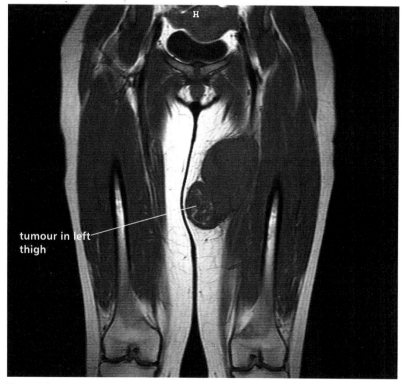

Figure 4.1 An MRI scan showing a tumour in the thigh.

tumour in left thigh

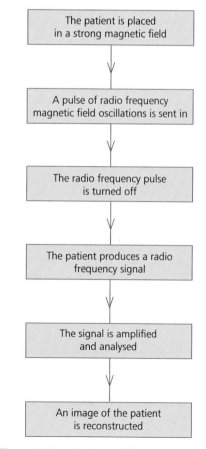

The patient is placed in a strong magnetic field

↓

A pulse of radio frequency magnetic field oscillations is sent in

↓

The radio frequency pulse is turned off

↓

The patient produces a radio frequency signal

↓

The signal is amplified and analysed

↓

An image of the patient is reconstructed

Figure 4.2 The basic steps in MRI.

The exact response (and therefore the MRI signal) depends on what the nuclei are and how they are located in the body. It is as if the body contains millions of tiny 'beacons', all ready to emit their signals to tell us where and what they are. Here, then, is an excellent tool for imaging. All that is required is some sophisticated computer back-up to process the complicated data emerging from the body.

Despite its relatively high cost, MRI has now become an indispensable imaging technique. With minimal risk to the patient, it can provide a wide range of information, including body anatomy, organ function, flow and biochemistry. The rest of this chapter will explain in detail how it all happens.

NUCLEAR MAGNETIC RESONANCE (NMR)

In MRI, a particular type of nucleus is selected and its distribution in the body is monitored. **Hydrogen** is the most commonly imaged element, not only due to its abundance in the body, but also because it gives the strongest MRI signal.

Proton spin

The nucleus of a hydrogen atom is a single proton. Such a proton is not stationary but **spins** about an axis as shown in figure 4.3. This spinning positive charge acts like a tiny current loop and consequently generates, along the spin axis, a magnetic field, M, just like that of a bar magnet.

The symbol M is chosen to represent the magnetic field generated by the spinning proton (its 'magnetisation'). This is partly to distinguish it from the applied magnetic fields, whose flux densities are given by the conventional symbol B, and partly to fall in line with the accepted notation used in MRI.

In a water rich substance like the human body, with its abundance of hydrogen, there are enormous numbers of such 'magnets'. Normally, they are orientated at random (figure 4.4(a)) and their individual magnetic fields tend to cancel out. However, if such a group of spinning protons is in an external magnetic field, of flux density B_0, they preferentially align themselves with the direction of the field (figure 4.4(b)). They may align themselves either parallel or anti-parallel to the field, and this constitutes two slightly different energy states E_1 and E_2 (figure 4.5(b)). The lower energy state E_1 corresponds to parallel alignment, and in equilibrium, more of the protons are found in this state.

> ### *Hydrogen in the body*
>
> Approximately a tenth of the average body mass is hydrogen. About 70% of this is contained in water molecules, 20% in fats and a small amount in proteins.

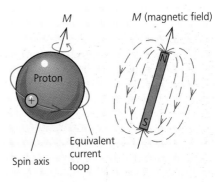

Figure 4.3 Proton spin.

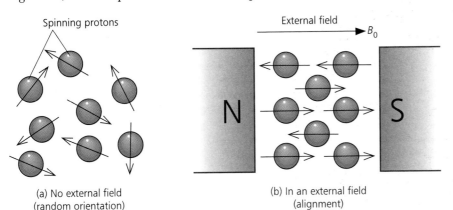

(a) No external field (random orientation)

(b) In an external field (alignment)

Figure 4.4 Proton alignment in an external magnetic field.

Proton energy levels

The concept of energy levels is not new. We are already familiar with the idea that the electrons orbiting a nucleus can only take up certain discrete, allowed energies in their orbits, i.e. their energy is **quantised**. These energy states can be represented on equivalent energy level diagrams (figure 4.5(a)). Transition between these energy levels can take place either by an electron *absorbing* a certain **quantum** of electromagnetic energy (excitation) or by an electron *emitting* such an allowed quantum (de-excitation).

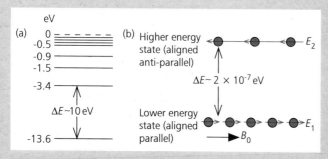

Figure 4.5 Comparison of (**a**) electron and (**b**) proton energy levels in the hydrogen atom.

The same model of quantised energy states applies to nuclei, and, in particular, to the hydrogen nucleus or proton. When in an external magnetic field, the proton can 'occupy' one of two possible energy states (figure 4.5(b)) corresponding to parallel and anti-parallel alignment with the field.

Transitions between these states can occur through the absorption or emission of a definite, quantised amount of energy ΔE. This corresponds to the proton 'flipping' between parallel and anti-parallel orientations. For hydrogen protons in a magnetic field of flux density 1T (a typical magnetic field used in MRI),

$$\Delta E = 1.76 \times 10^{-7} \, \text{eV} \qquad \textbf{(about 0.2 μeV)}$$

(Compare this value with the ΔE of about 10 eV between the ground and first excited states of the *electronic* energy levels in the hydrogen atom!)

Although this is an insignificant amount of energy on an atomic or molecular scale, it is nevertheless vital in the production of an MRI signal. It corresponds to a photon frequency of

$$f = \frac{\Delta E}{h}$$

where
$$\Delta E = 1.76 \times 10^{-7} \times 1.6 \times 10^{-19} \, \text{J}$$

$$f = \frac{1.76 \times 10^{-7} \times 1.6 \times 10^{-19} \, \text{J}}{6.63 \times 10^{-34} \, \text{J s}}$$

$$= 4.25 \times 10^{7} \, \text{Hz}$$

$$= 42.5 \, \text{MHz}$$

This radiation is in the **radio frequency** band of the electromagnetic spectrum. Transitions between the proton energy levels can thus be made by absorbing or emitting photons of this frequency.

Thermal excitation of protons between the energy levels is also possible at body temperatures (due to the small value of ΔE) and results in almost half of the protons occupying the higher energy (anti-parallel) state. Such protons can also 'flip back' to their lower energy (parallel) state by releasing their energy to the surrounding atoms.

Precession

Consider a spinning top, perfectly balanced and spinning about a vertical axis, parallel to the gravitational field (figure 4.6(a)). If it is displaced a little from this axis, it does not immediately topple over, but instead it slowly rotates or **precesses** about its original spin axis (figure 4.6(b)).

So it is with the spinning protons. Instead of aligning perfectly with the external magnetic field B_0, they steadily precess about its direction (figure 4.7). They do so with an angular frequency ω (radians per second) which is directly proportional to B_0 (Tesla).

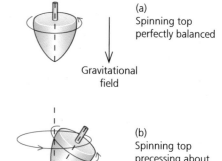

Figure 4.6 Precession of a spinning top in a gravitational field: (**a**) perfectly balanced; (**b**) precessing.

Thus

$$\omega \propto B_0$$
$$\textbf{or} \quad \omega = \gamma B_0$$

where γ is a constant called the **gyromagnetic ratio**.
If we work in terms of frequency f (Hz) and use the expression

$$f = \frac{\omega}{2\pi}$$

we obtain

$$f = \frac{\gamma B_0}{2\pi}$$

a frequency known as the **Larmor frequency**.

The constant $\frac{\gamma}{2\pi}$ has a value of 42.57 MHz T^{-1} for hydrogen protons.

For these particles, the so-called **Larmor equation** can thus be written as

$$f = 42.57\, B_0 \text{ MHz} \qquad (4.1)$$

For the large magnetic fields of 1 or 2 T encountered in MRI, f is of the order of 50 MHz, which lies in the radio frequency range.

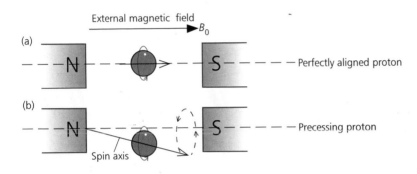

Figure 4.7 Precession of a proton in a magnetic field: **(a)** perfectly aligned; **(b)** precessing.

Larmor frequency – Worked example

Calculate the frequency of precession of hydrogen protons in a magnetic field of flux density 1.5 T.

(If γ is the gyromagnetic ratio, the value of $\frac{\gamma}{2\pi}$ for hydrogen protons = 42.57 MHz T^{-1}).

Using the Larmor equation (4.1):

$$f = \frac{\gamma B_0}{2\pi}$$
$$= 42.57 \text{ MHz T}^{-1} \times 1.5 \text{ T}$$
$$= 63.9 \text{ MHz} \qquad (3\text{sf})$$

This frequency lies in the **radio frequency** range.

Simple experimental model of proton precession

This demonstration may be presented quite simply using an overhead projector, if a plotting compass with transparent faces is used.

The small plotting compass is positioned in the magnetic field B_0 of a bar magnet and displays alignment with the field (figure 4.8(a)).

Very briefly, a second small bar magnet is introduced and then removed along a perpendicular (lateral) direction, and the compass needle is seen to oscillate about B_0 (figure 4.8(b)). (The compass needle is behaving like the disturbed protons and 'precesses'.)

If the field B_0 at the plotting compass is reduced, by moving the (longitudinal) magnet further away (figure 4.8(c)) and the process is repeated, the compass needle is seen to oscillate at a lower frequency. Hence, the dependence of the Larmor precessional frequency on field is clearly illustrated.

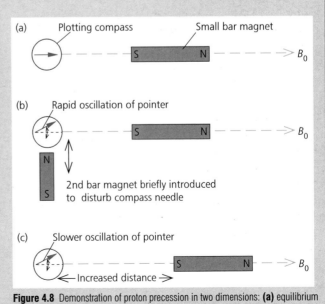

Figure 4.8 Demonstration of proton precession in two dimensions: **(a)** equilibrium alignment in the external field B_0; **(b)** 'precession' of compass needle about B_0 when disturbed from equilibrium; **(c)** effect of decreasing the field at the compass.

Resonance

An oscillating system possesses its own **natural frequency**. If it is **forced** to oscillate by an external periodic stimulus, it will respond best when the forcing frequency equals its natural frequency. This is the phenomenon of **resonance**. (An example is a child on a swing, synchronising his 'push' with the natural frequency of the swing, to get maximum height.)

The precessing protons possess their own natural frequency, the Larmor frequency f, which depends only on the *size* of the applied field, B_0, and not on their inclinations to it. If an external stimulus of exactly this frequency f is applied, the protons resonate, absorb the energy and can 'flip' to a higher energy state. Such a stimulus is applied in the form of a **pulse** of radio frequency (rf) magnetic field oscillations.

Not only does this pulse excite the protons to 'flip', but also it forces them to precess **in phase** with it, and thus with each other (figure 4.9(b)). This is *crucial*, since this precession in phase is the origin of the **MRI signal**.

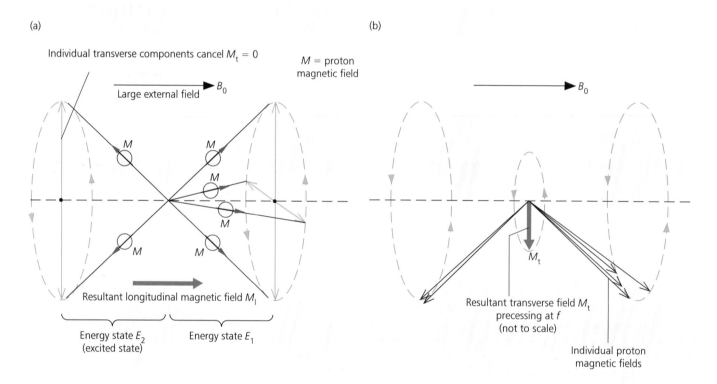

Figure 4.9 Transverse and longitudinal magnetic fields, due to spinning protons: **(a)** random phase of precessing protons gives only a resultant longitudinal magnetic field M_l; **(b)** protons precessing in phase give rise to a transverse magnetic field M_t.

Where does the MRI signal come from?

When in the external field B_0, more protons are in the lower energy state E_1 than in E_2. Hence, there is a small resultant **longitudinal magnetic field** M_l developed by the protons, parallel to B_0 (figure 4.9(a)). This, however, cannot be measured since it is parallel to the large externally applied field B_0.

Before the application of the rf pulse, when the protons are precessing 'out of step' with each other, they generate no resultant magnetic field in the **transverse** direction (perpendicular to their spinning axis) as all the tiny components of their magnetic fields cancel out in this direction (figure 4.9(a)). However, when they are *forced* to precess in phase (or 'in step') by the stimulating rf frequency pulse, all their transverse components add up (figure 4.9(b)). This produces a **transverse magnetic field** M_t which precesses about the main spinning axis at the same (Larmor) frequency as the protons. Here, at last, is a signal we can measure!

Typical rf pulses

When an rf pulse is applied, the resultant proton magnetic field (the vector sum of the longitudinal (M_l) and transverse (M_t) components) is deviated from the longitudinal axis through an angle that depends on the strength and duration of the incident rf pulse.

If the so-called flip angle is 90° (figure 4.10) M_t becomes zero (there are equal numbers of protons in the parallel and anti-parallel states E_1 and E_2) leaving M_t alone precessing at the Larmor frequency. The stimulating rf pulse, of typically less than 50 μs duration, is then called a **90° pulse**.

A pulse of twice this duration (or strength) however, will have enough energy to excite all the 'proton magnets' to the higher anti-parallel state. This flips the magnetic field vector through 180° and is known as a **180° pulse**.

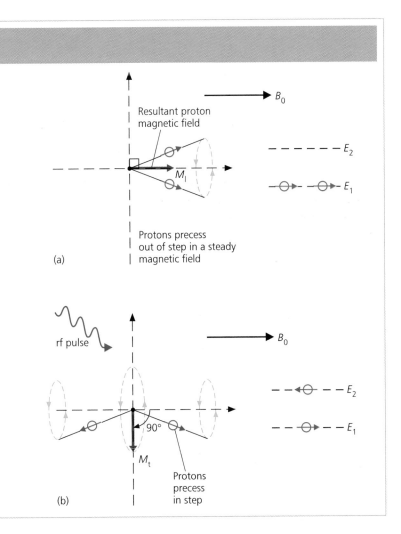

(a)

(b)

Figure 4.10 (a) Before and **(b)** after the application of a 90° pulse.

Detection of the MRI signal

According to the laws of **electromagnetic induction**, if a conductor is placed in a changing magnetic field, an e.m.f. will be *induced* in the conductor. The *precessing* transverse magnetic field M_t constitutes a *changing* magnetic field and hence can induce a small e.m.f. (of the order of microvolts) in a detector coil positioned outside the patient. This forms the **MRI signal**, and its frequency is still the same radio frequency (the Larmor frequency) as that previously applied as the stimulating pulse.

Figure 4.11 summarises the various processes taking place in the generation of the final MRI signal. What we now have to establish is:

- how to find out exactly where in the body the signal is coming from, in order to build up an image, and
- how to distinguish between protons in different tissue types to develop **contrast**.

These are no mean tasks!

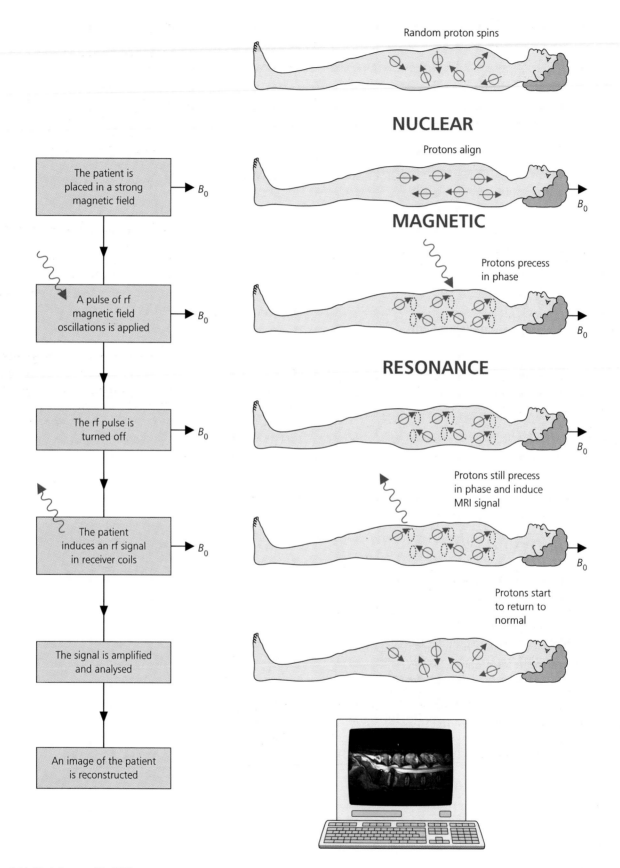

Figure 4.11 Block diagram of the NMR process.

LOCALISATION OF THE SIGNAL

First, a plane of interest in the body is selected for investigation. The MRI signal strength is established at various coordinates within that plane, and these are synchronised and displayed on a visual display unit (VDU). In MRI, bright areas on the display correspond to large signal strengths and dark areas represent small responses.

Slice selection

The determination of 'slice' or plane of interest is achieved using the fact that the Larmor frequency f of the protons is directly proportional to the applied steady external field B_0.

$$f = \frac{\gamma B_0}{2\pi}$$

If a slightly different value of B_0 is applied to different sections of the body, each section will have its own individual Larmor frequency f, which will differ from that of its neighbours. When an rf pulse of *specific frequency f* is transmitted into the body, only those protons having *exactly* the same precession frequency f will **resonate**. Protons in neighbouring slices will be relatively unaffected, thus providing a method for identifying the slice of interest.

Rf pulse shape

In practice, the rf pulse contains a small range of frequencies, known as the **bandwidth**. For example, at a Larmor frequency of 64 MHz, the bandwidth is typically 1 kHz, producing resonance over a very restricted slice width. The rf pulse itself is shaped by varying its amplitude in time.

The variation in the value of external field applied is achieved using **gradient field coils**. These superimpose a regularly increasing magnetic field ΔB onto the fixed (and very uniform) magnetic field B_0 applied to the whole body (figure 4.12(a)). Thus

$$B_{\text{total}} = \underset{\text{(fixed)}}{B_0} + \underset{\text{(spatially varying)}}{\Delta B}$$

This **slice selection gradient** is shown as being applied along the longitudinal axis, but any axis may be selected.

Thus, if slice XX is chosen, a gradient field of $0.01\,\text{T m}^{-1}$ ($10\,\text{mT m}^{-1}$) is applied, and a narrow frequency band rf pulse of 64.3 MHz is transmitted into the body. Protons in the selected slice then resonate and induce an MRI signal in the detector coil.

In practice, the gradient field is not applied quite like this. Using pairs of coils that produce magnetic fields that can either *add to* or *subtract from* the main field, a gradient field like that shown in figure 4.12(b) is commonly employed (see also figure 4.26 on page 89).

MRI

- Most MRI studies image **hydrogen** in the body.
- Its nucleus (a single **proton**) **spins** generating a tiny **magnetic field**.
- When in a **large, external magnetic field B_0**, the protons **align** and **precess** about B_0, at a frequency called the **Larmor frequency**, f:

$$f = \frac{\gamma B_0}{2\pi}$$

and lie in the **radio frequency (rf) range**.

- If an **rf pulse** of this frequency is sent into the body, the spinning protons **resonate** and precess in phase.
- This generates a transverse magnetic field M_t that precesses at the same Larmor frequency.
- When the rf pulse is switched off, the precessing M_t of the protons **induces** an e.m.f. in a detector coil outside the patient. This is the **MRI signal**.

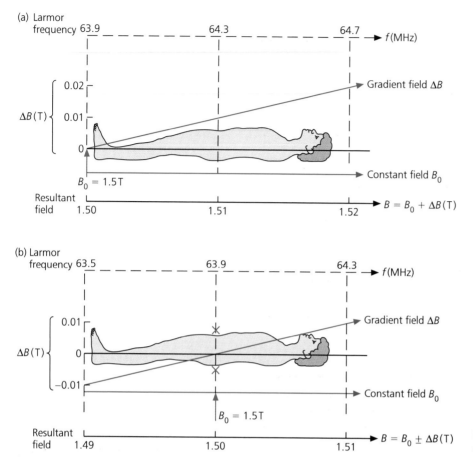

Figure 4.12 Slice selection: **(a)** simple gradient field; **(b)** commonly-used gradient field.

Gradient field – Worked example

A patient of height 1.8 m is placed horizontally in a uniform magnetic field of flux density 1.5 T directed from his feet to his head. A gradient field of $0.01\,\mathrm{T\,m^{-1}}$ is applied horizontally, again from his feet to his head.

If $\dfrac{\gamma}{2\pi}$ is $42.57\,\mathrm{MHz\,T^{-1}}$, (where γ is the gyromagnetic ratio) estimate the frequency of the transmitted rf pulse required to produce proton resonance in a slice through his abdomen, 0.9 m from his feet.

The frequency required for resonance is given by:

$$f = \frac{\gamma B}{2\pi}$$
$$= 42.57\,\mathbf{MHz\ T^{-1}} \times \mathbf{B}$$

The field B at the selected slice:

$$= B_0 + \Delta B$$
$$B = 1.5\,\mathbf{T} + (0.9\,\mathbf{m} \times 0.01\,\mathbf{T\,m^{-1}})$$
$$B = 1.509\,\mathbf{T}$$

Therefore
$$f = 42.57\,\mathbf{MHz\,T^{-1}} \times 1.509\,\mathbf{T}$$
$$= 64.24\,\mathbf{MHz} \quad \text{(4sf)}$$

Thus, an rf pulse of 64.24 MHz will produce resonance in the selected 'slice'

Localisation within a slice

Once the slice has been identified, we then need to locate exactly *where in the slice* the MRI signal is coming from. This requires two further small gradient fields across the slice (figure 4.13).

The slice (for example XX in figure 4.12) is first divided up into individual elements, called **pixels**, each having its own set of coordinates. Although only a 5×5 matrix is illustrated here, typical arrays will contain 256×256 pixels. High resolution studies may employ a 512×512 matrix, whilst fast imaging sequences may only use 128×128 arrays.

One gradient field (for instance applied along an 'x-axis', B_x) establishes a specific **frequency** for each x-coordinate, in a similar way to the action of the slice selection gradient. (Each *column* on the diagram corresponds to a particular frequency, rather like the keys on a piano: the pitch of the note heard identifies which key was struck.) The frequencies differ by only small amounts from the basic resonant frequency selected for the slice, so they still lie within the bandwidth of the receiver amplifiers and are detected.

The other gradient field (along a 'y-axis', B_y) modifies the **phase** of the precessing protons. It is applied for a short time and gets the protons out of step, or phase, with each other by an amount depending on the value of the gradient field at that point. Protons in a larger field (top *rows* on figure 4.13) get a bigger 'kick' than those in a smaller field and consequently suffer larger phase changes.

The resultant signal from the slice is complicated! It consists of different frequencies and different phases, but using a mathematical analysis technique, called Fourier transformations, and powerful computers, the signal is sorted and digitised. Each pixel is attributed with an appropriate signal intensity and an image can be reconstructed on a VDU.

Figure 4.13 Signal localisation within a single slice.

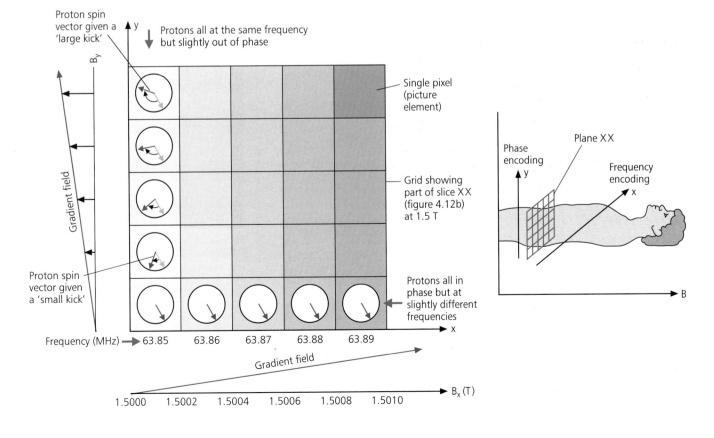

FACTORS INFLUENCING SIGNAL INTENSITY

We have already established that large MRI signal intensities produce *bright* areas and small signals produce *dark* regions on the final image, but what factors actually determine the signal strength and whether the image will look black or white? Unlike X-ray images, where such contrast is determined by only one thing (X-ray attenuation) the MRI signal is influenced by at least ten factors!

Of these, the most important are:

- **proton density:** the greater the number of hydrogen protons, the larger the signal (no hydrogen, no signal!). In all MRI images, air and outer bone areas, having no hydrogen, thus appear dark
- **tissue type:** its composition, structure and surroundings
- **rf pulse sequence:** this 'favours' certain tissues above others, thereby introducing **contrast**.

Interpretation of the final image is a highly skilled task. The same body structure can look white on one image, yet black on another, depending on the precise technique employed (figure 4.14).

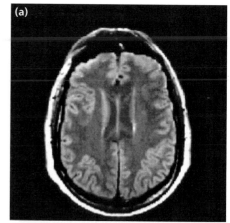

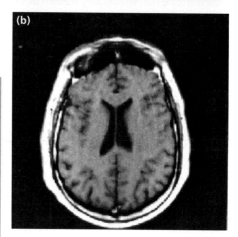

Proton density

The extent to which the protons in hydrogen atoms resonate in NMR depends not only on their numbers, but also on their **mobility**. Protons in large molecules do not contribute very much, since they are relatively immobile.

The highest proton density signals come from relatively 'free' body water, like cerebrospinal fluid (CSF) in the brain and spinal column, urine and other fluids. Various tissues, such as kidney, spleen and brain come next, followed by cartilage, membranes, and finally bone and air.

Table 4.1 displays approximate percentages of water in the body, which provides a reasonable indication of expected proton density signal.

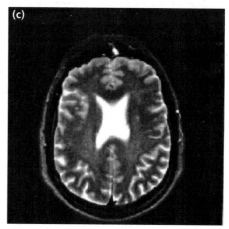

Figure 4.14 Three transverse MRI scans through the *same* normal head: **(a)** proton density weighted; **(b)** T_1-weighted; **(c)** T_2-weighted.

Body material	% water content
air	0
bone	12
liver	71
muscle	79
heart	83
brain grey matter	84
white matter	71

Table 4.1 Water content in the body.

On a 'proton-density image', 'free' water appears bright, air spaces and bone appear black, and soft tissue is quite bright with poor discrimination.

Which of the brain images in figure 4.14 would *you* think is a proton density weighted image?

Relaxation

Imagine yourself in an excited state! In order to return to 'normal', you need to release some energy somehow. You need to *relax*.

This is precisely what the excited protons try to do when the stimulating rf pulse is turned off. They attempt to return to their original 'normal' orientation in the B_0 field, by giving up the extra energy they acquired from the rf pulse, to their neighbouring atoms, in a process known as **relaxation** (figure 4.15). Not only do the protons 'flip back' to parallel (low energy state) alignment with B_0, but also they start to precess out of phase again. The latter results in a decrease in the transverse proton magnetic field M_t, which in turn *reduces the MRI signal*.

The ease with which the adjacent atoms can absorb the surplus energy depends on the exact nature of the tissue, and gives us a way of distinguishing one type of tissue from another. In other words, relaxation is the key to providing **tissue contrast** in MRI.

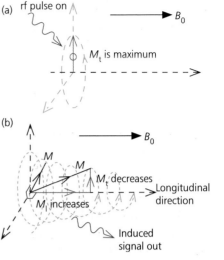

Figure 4.15 Relaxation: **(a)** excitation; **(b)** relaxation.

Relaxation processes

Longitudinal relaxation (T_1 recovery)

The longitudinal magnetic field (M_l) increases to its original higher value, as excited protons flip back from the higher (anti-parallel) states, E_2, to the lower (parallel) ones, E_1. The **recovery** is exponential and is characterised by a **longitudinal relaxation time, T_1** (figure 4.16(b)). During T_1 (typically about a second) about two-thirds of the energy is lost from the spinning protons to the surrounding molecules (the so-called **spin-lattice interaction**).

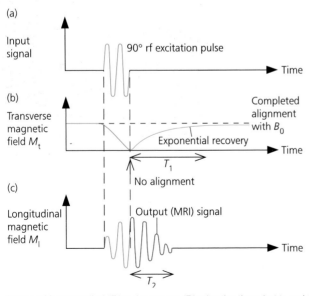

Figure 4.16 Longitudinal (T_1) and transverse (T_2) relaxation times (not to scale).

Values of T_1 depend on the 'energy match' with the surrounding molecules, which all have their own natural frequencies of oscillation. If these are close to the Larmor frequency of the spinning protons, energy is more rapidly released to the surroundings, reducing T_1.

Such is the case for the larger molecules or for *bound* water molecules (which move more slowly than free water molecules). Fat, liver and spleen all have relatively short values of T_1.

Transverse relaxation (T_2 decay)

When the forcing rf pulse is removed, there is a tendency for the precessing protons to become out of step (or phase) again. They do so by exchanging energy with each other, a **spin-spin interaction**. This results in a decrease or **decay** in the transverse magnetic field M_t, with a characteristic time T_2 which is generally much shorter than T_1 (approximately 50 ms) (figure 4.16(c)). T_2 describes the time required to reduce M_t to about a third of its original value. Since the induced e.m.f. (or MRI signal) is determined by M_t, the MRI signal decays at the same rate.

If the *range* of natural frequencies of adjacent nuclei is large, the spins de-phase very rapidly and T_2 is short. This is the case with solids and larger molecules, such as in tendons, muscle and liver.

Contrast

We can exploit the differences in relaxation times between tissues, to provide **contrast**, by carefully controlling the amount of *time* we give the tissues to relax.

It is rather like a team on a strict training programme. After a period of intensive exercise, the assembled squad is given time to 'relax'. Some members of the squad will relax quickly and be fully recovered after 10 minutes, ready to begin the next session. Others, however, take longer to regain their strength, and when the next session re-starts after 10 minutes, they begin at less than 100% fitness. If this training regime continues repeatedly, the 'output' from the team members will vary enormously!

In a similar way, we *repeatedly* excite the protons (apply rf pulses), allow them to relax (release energy to the surroundings and each other) and measure their output (switch on the locating gradient fields). By adjusting the time allowed for relaxation, one medium, with its characteristic relaxation times, may be enhanced rather than another. Contrast is thus achieved (figure 4.17).

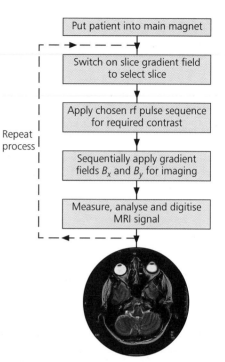

Figure 4.17 Block diagram of the MRI process.

Pulse sequences

Specific **pulse sequences** are selected, whereby rf pulses repeated at particular **repetition rates** give the desired MR image, with its particular contrast characteristics.

- T_1-**weighted images** – these use rapidly repeated pulses, enhancing the brightness of tissues with **short values of T_1** (e.g. fat, larger molecules). Watery substances appear dark.
- T_2-**weighted images** – by delaying the application of the gradient fields (B_x and B_y) by maybe 30 ms, before obtaining the MRI signal, tissues with **long values of T_2** (e.g. 'watery tissues', diseased tissues) are favoured, and appear bright.
- **Proton-density-weighted images** – these depend little on T_1 or T_2 but highlight the density of mobile protons and hence water content (e.g. urine, cerebrospinal fluid).

Refer back to figure 4.14 and predict which of the images are T_1 and T_2 weighted.

As a very 'rough guide', T_1-weighted images are useful for observing body *structure*, since they provide excellent soft-tissue detail (e.g. between the white and grey matter of the brain). On the other hand, T_2-weighted images are preferred for investigating *diseased* areas, as fluids (often indicative of disease) appear bright (figure 4.18).

Further details about pulse sequences may be found on the Web page.

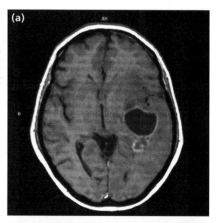

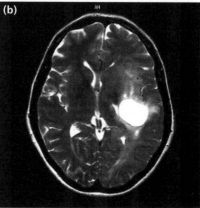

Figure 4.18 Cross-section of a brain with a cyst. On a T_1-weighted image **(a)** the cyst thus appears dark, whereas on a T_2-weighted image **(b)** it appears bright. Skill with image interpretation is clearly vital!

Resolution

Resolution describes the *fineness of detail* observed in the image. It is determined largely by the uniformity of the fields and the size of the gradient fields.

If a large gradient field is employed, for example in slice selection, there will be correspondingly large differences in *B* and the resonant frequency, *f*, for small changes in axial distance along the patient. This reduces the thickness of the slice over which resonance occurs, thus improving resolution. For example, in brain scans, the slice thickness is typically 1–5 mm, and a resolution of less than 1 mm is achieved within the slice. (The latter 'in-plane' resolution is not only improved by using larger gradient fields, but also by increasing the time for which the signal is sampled.)

Clarity of image also depends on how much 'background noise' is displayed. This is described using the **signal-to-noise ratio (SNR)**, which ideally should be high. It may be increased by

- increasing the main magnetic field strength, *B*
- siting the receiver coils as close to the body section as possible
- using small receiver coils.

For instance, small body-shaped coils can be employed in certain regions like the extremities, yielding resolutions of about 0.1 mm (figures 4.19).

There are, however, disadvantages to using ever-increasing values of *B*, including increased cost, more problems with rf penetration and coil construction, and also greater power deposition in the body due to the rf power requirements.

Figure 4.19 A knee coil.

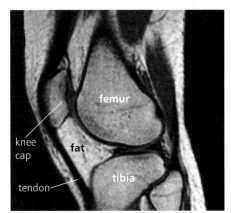

Figure 4.20 An MRI image of the knee.

Resolution – Worked example

For a particular brain scan, a slice thickness of 2 mm is specified. A slice gradient field of 0.01 T m⁻¹ is used. Estimate the necessary bandwidth (frequency range) necessary in the applied rf pulse.

(Assume $\frac{\gamma}{2\pi}$ is 42.6 MHz T⁻¹ where γ is the gyromagnetic ratio)

The change in magnetic field over a distance of 2 mm is given by

$$\Delta B = 2 \times 10^{-3}\,\text{m} \times 0.01\,\text{T m}^{-1}$$
$$= 2 \times 10^{-5}\,\text{T}$$

The corresponding change in Larmor frequency is then

$$\Delta f = \frac{\gamma \Delta B}{2\pi}$$
$$= 42.6\,\text{MHz T}^{-1} \times 2 \times 10^{-5}\,\text{T}$$
$$= 8.52 \times 10^{-4}\,\text{MHz}$$

This is the necessary frequency range (very approximately 1 kHz).

THE MR *IMAGE*

- **Rf signals** from the body are used to build up an image.
- Their origins are located using three perpendicular **gradient fields**.
- The **signal strength** depends on: **proton density** (hydrogen concentration) **tissue type** (structure and surroundings) **pulse sequence** (duration and repetition rate of the stimulating rf pulses).
- **Relaxation** (process by which excited protons release their surplus energy to their surroundings) determines **contrast**.
- **Resolution** improved using: **large** and **uniform main magnetic field *B***, **large gradient fields**, **small receiver coils** close to the body.

INSTRUMENTATION AND EQUIPMENT

The installation of an MRI unit is a very complex and costly business, but despite this, there are now well over 100 modern, compact units operating throughout the UK. Of the initial cost (approximately £2 million) more than half is attributable to the main magnet. Running costs (including replenishing the coolants) can then amount to around £400 per examination.

It is the availability of massive computer power that renders fast (and hence approximately real-time) high-resolution imaging possible. A computer is thus at the heart of any MRI system (figure 4.21).

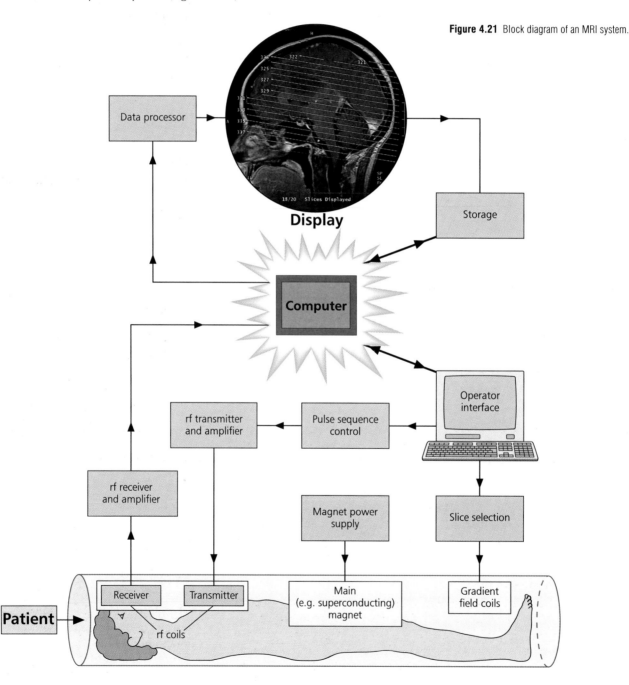

Figure 4.21 Block diagram of an MRI system.

The main magnet

This is perhaps the most important part of the MRI machine. Not only must it supply high magnetic flux densities of generally between 0.2 and 2 T (more than 10 000 times the Earth's magnetic flux density!), but also its field must be very **homogeneous** (uniform) over a volume large enough to take a patient.

The magnets available can be divided into three types, namely **permanent**, **resistive** and **superconducting** (table 4.2).

Table 4.2 Comparisons of magnets.

	Permanent	Resistive (electromagnet)	Superconducting
magnetic field	cannot be switched off	easily switched on and off	switched on and off with long delays
magnetic field lines	vertical	horizontal (can be vertical if required)	horizontal
power supply	none	large	small
running costs	low	high (electricity)	medium (coolants)
mass	80 tonnes	2 tonnes	6 tonnes
installation costs	medium	low	high
fringe (surrounding) field	small	large	large
magnetic field strength	low $< {\sim}0.3$ T	medium < 0.5 T	high 0.5–2.5 T(clinical) < 9 T (spectroscopy)
image quality	reasonable	good	excellent
scan times	long	long	short

Permanent magnets

The most common material used to construct permanent magnets is **alnico**, an alloy of aluminium, nickel and cobalt, although research is constantly undertaken to develop new materials for improved magnetic performance.

Due to their greater weight only low field strengths (typically 0.2 T) can be achieved, but the field is more easily confined than in other magnets, reducing shielding problems. Furthermore, they have large apertures so are less claustrophobic for patients (figure 4.22).

Resistive (electro) magnets

A regularly wound coil of copper, carrying a direct current, generates a uniform magnetic field along its axis (figure 4.23). Such an **electromagnet** is sometimes referred to as a **resistive** magnet, due to the resistance (and consequently resistive energy losses) in the coils.

Although its capital cost is low, its operation costs are high due to the large power consumed. Typically, a 0.15 T machine operates at about 80 kW, of which about 50 kW is dissipated as heat in the windings! This heat is removed by pumping water rapidly (up to 150 litres per minute) through the hollow coils. Its great advantage is that it can be turned on and off easily.

Superconducting magnets

A material becomes **superconducting** (it has zero electrical resistance) when its temperature falls below a certain value, called the **critical temperature**. An alloy of niobium and titanium has a critical temperature just below 10 K, and is widely used to make the coils of superconducting magnets (figure 4.24). The shape of the resulting magnetic field is the same as that from ordinary resistive (electro) magnets, but the flux density is considerably higher, since much larger currents are used.

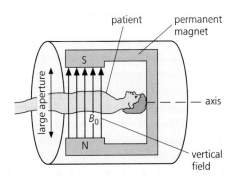

Figure 4.22 Permanent magnet.

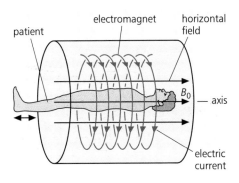

Figure 4.23 Resistive (electro) magnet.

The current is switched on to create the magnetic field. The coils are supercooled using **cryogens** (coolants, usually liquid helium and liquid nitrogen) thus **ramping** up the flux density to its final value in a matter of hours.

The tremendous advantages offered by superconducting magnets are very *large, homogeneous magnetic fields*, sustained with very *little power input*.

Set against this are the drawbacks of very costly manufacture and installation, due to the coolant system, which makes it larger and heavier than a resistive magnet, together with very long start-up times.

Superconductivity

Superconductivity was discovered by Omnes in 1911, three years after he first achieved liquefaction of helium (4 K). It was not until such low temperatures were available that the phenomenon of superconductivity could be observed.

It has long been known that the resistance of a metal decreases with temperature. However, as the temperature approaches absolute zero, some substances (pure metals, alloys and some compounds) exhibit **zero** d.c. electrical resistance – they become **superconducting**. It is a **quantum mechanical** effect, and in simple terms is due to the crystal lattice being unable at these low temperatures to take energy from the drifting electrons. Since resistance only arises because energy is lost from the electrons to the lattice, the resistance becomes zero.

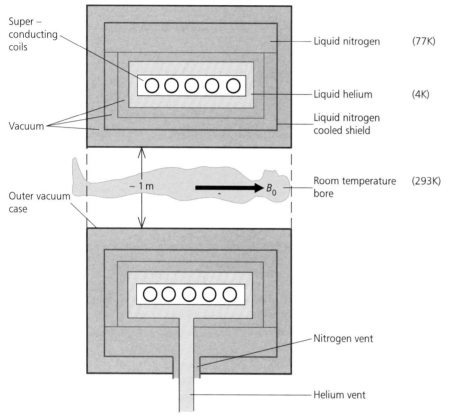

Figure 4.24 Cross section through a superconducting magnet.

Cooling the superconducting magnet

Various cooling 'layers' are necessary (figure 4.24(b)):

- the superconducting coils are maintained well below their critical temperature by surrounding them with a tank of **liquid helium** (4 K)
- to reduce rapid evaporation of the expensive liquid helium, an outer coolant of **liquid nitrogen** is employed (77 K)
- the space around the tanks of cryogens is insulated by a **vacuum**.

Inevitably, there is some heat flow into the cryogens, which therefore need 'topping up', typically every few weeks for nitrogen and every few months for helium. Great care is needed to prevent air entering the system, as this would solidify forming a plug.

Magnetic flux density

The magnetic flux density B along the axis of a coil is given by

$$B = \mu_0 n I$$

where μ_0 is the permeability of free space, n is the number of turns per unit length of the coil and I is the current. Hence, the larger the current, the stronger is the field.

Gradient fields

These are required to **localise** the MRI signal. They need to provide magnetic flux densities increasing uniformly with distance along a given axis. How would **you** do it?

The easy solution is to use a conventional electromagnet in which the number of turns per metre increases linearly with distance along its axis (figure 4.25(a)). A more sophisticated approach, yielding more reliable gradient fields, uses pairs of oppositely wound coils as shown in figure 4.25(b).

In either case, a linear magnetic field gradient is established along a chosen axis, and its size can be adjusted using the current flowing through the coils.

Figure 4.25 (a) Simple gradient field; **(b)** commonly used gradient field.

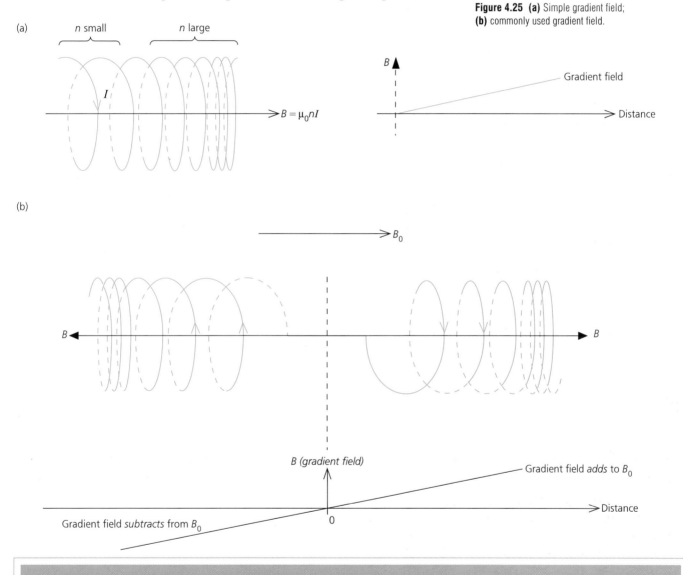

Gradient fields

The maximum amplitude of the magnetic field gradient varies for the different axes, ranging from typically 1% of the main magnet strength (approximately $10\,\text{mT}\,\text{m}^{-1}$) for the slice selection gradient to lower values for the other axes.

They need to switch on and off rapidly (approximately 1 ms or less) to allow fast pulse repetition rates and therefore shorter scan times. This rapid switching is responsible for the loud bangs heard during a scan.

Radio frequency coils

These coils generate (**transmitter coil**) and detect (**receiver coil**) the rf pulses fundamental to the MRI signal and are tuned, like a radio, to the selected resonant frequency. Because there is a time delay (of more than 1 ms) between transmission and reception of signals, they are often the *same* coils, called **transceivers**.

The coils must be orientated to provide and detect magnetic fields at right angles to the main magnetic field, and are usually arranged to surround the part of the body to be imaged. For example, the **body coil** is a transmitter for *all* types of examination and also a receiver when larger parts of the body are being imaged, whilst the **head coil** (figure 4.26) acts as **receiver only**.

To achieve improved image quality for superficial areas (e.g. the spine, wrist or knee) **surface receiver** coils of different shapes, corresponding to local body contours, are sometimes used (see figure 4.19). Deeper structures (>0.1 m) cannot, however, be examined with these coils.

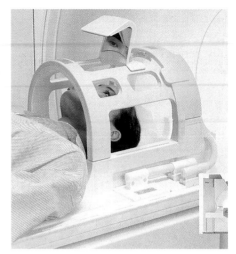

Figure 4.26 Head coil.

Rf circuits

The **rf transmitter** is normally part of a tuned circuit and produces pulses of the required frequency, amplitude, phase, bandwidth and repetition rate. These are then **amplified** and passed through an **rf monitor**, which ensures the delivery of safe levels of rf power to the patient.

The **rf receiver** registers the basic MRI signal, which is typically of the order of a few μV. **The rf receiver amplifier** needs to provide a gain of about 10^6 to achieve the few volts output necessary for the analogue to digital converters.

Data processing and storage

MRI signal analysis and digitisation is achieved through the main computer and then presented for display or storage.

The final image may be displayed in any chosen plane, since the 3-D information is available, and furthermore special pulse sequences can be used to give 3-D images directly. Even approximately real-time imaging is possible since the computer analysis is so fast.

Colour displays are also now available in addition to the traditional 'grey scale' images showing contrast (figure 4.27).

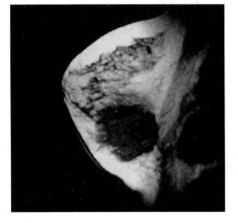
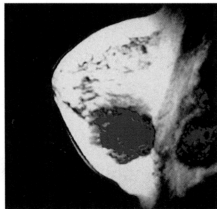

Figure 4.27 The use of colour helps to clarify the tumour location and extent in the breast.

Site planning

All MRI systems have considerable structural limitations on their installation and use, demanding large scan rooms with reinforced floors to take the weight of the main magnet. The large magnetic field of the latter imposes further restrictions.

Magnetic shielding

Any magnetic field 'straying' outside the MR scan room (sometimes referred to as **stray** or **fringe fields**) can be a major problem for other hospital equipment, such as CT scanners and image intensifiers (X-ray department), radioactive counting equipment and γ-cameras (nuclear medicine), linear accelerators (radiotherapy) and of course computers everywhere.

In addition, any rf fields 'straying' *into* the scan room, for example from lifts, computers and other electrical equipment, can seriously effect the MR image. Efficient magnetic shielding is essential.

- **Passive shielding** – the MR scan room is completely lined with steel. Windows have a conductive mesh and doors are protected with copper seals (i.e. conductive rather than magnetic materials).
- **Active shielding** – additional magnetic fields are used to provide a 'shielding magnetic field' and hence counteract the main applied field.

Patient transportation

All systems use a hydraulically or mechanically driven couch to slide the patient into the main bore of the magnet. Such systems must of course, be magnetically safe and contain no magnetic parts.

THE MRI UNIT

- An MRI unit is complex and costly (approximately £2m).
- Its major components are the: **main magnet**, ($\sim 0.2 \rightarrow 2$ T), which may be permanent, resistive or superconducting, **three gradient coils** producing gradient fields (~ 10 mT m^{-1}) in perpendicular directions, **radio frequency coils** (transmitter, receiver or both) perpendicular to the main magnetic field, **main computer** which controls the input settings, and analyses and displays the received **MRI signal**.
- **Site planning** demands: large scan rooms with **reinforced** floors, **magnetic shielding** around the scan room, **non-magnetic equipment**, (e.g. patient couch).

Special systems

MRI guided surgery can now take place through the development of **open magnets**. For example, focused ultrasound beams have been used to destroy tumours, using MRI guidance (figure 4.28). Surgical tools, of course, have to be non-magnetic.

Mobile MRI units are available but pose additional problems. The unit has to comply with road traffic regulations, such as weight and wheel base area, as well as having a very restricted fringe field. In practice, fields less than 0.5 T are employed and the parking area must be strong and level!

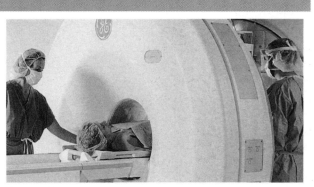

Figure 4.28 MRI-guided ultrasound surgery.

APPLICATIONS OF MRI

Historically, MRI began in the central nervous system, but it has now extended to all regions of the body. The *excellent resolution* and *contrast* available, *in any chosen plane* in the body, makes MRI an invaluable diagnostic tool with which to study body structure, function and chemistry, as well as disease.

Body water

Any increase in local body water results in higher proton density and T_2 weighted MRI signals. Swelling, infection, inflammation, bleeding, and cysts all lead to increased signals, whilst scar formation, fibrosis and calcification result in smaller values. These conditions can thus be diagnosed.

Brain and spinal cord

To date, this has been the most successfully studied region. The ability to produce 'slices' at any chosen angle, with excellent resolution and contrast (figure 4.29) makes MRI ideal for detecting tumours and other neurological diseases.

White and grey matter, blood and cerebrospinal fluid (CSF) are clearly identified, but the exact image depends on the pulse sequence used.

Joints

MRI is particularly useful in the analysis of joints, such as the ankle, knee or shoulder, where body tissues like muscles, ligaments, tendons and cartilage are clearly visualised in great detail (figures 4.20 and 4.30).

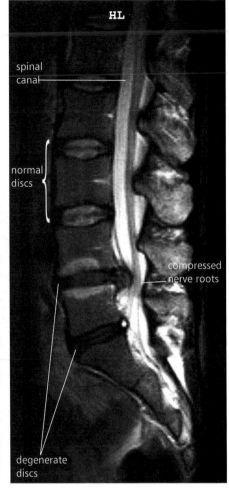

Figure 4.29 Spinal column – this patient suffers from sciatica. The upper discs are normal, showing some water content (white), whilst the bottom two are not – they are degenerate. These two protrude into the spinal canal (white), compressing the nerve roots (grey), thus causing pain.

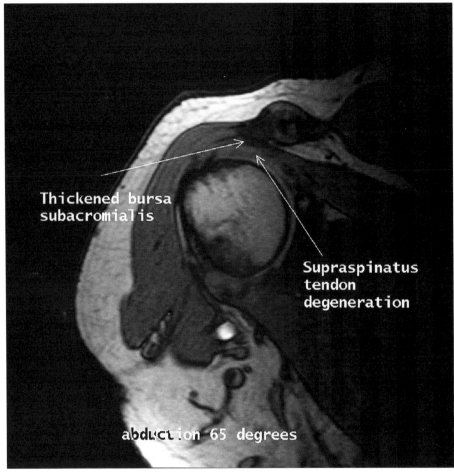

Figure 4.30 The shoulder structure is seen in great detail, here showing damage to the tendon.

Abdomen and pelvic organs

Structures like the **liver**, **pancreas**, **bladder** and **kidney** are increasingly being studied using MRI. There is good (T_1-weighted) contrast, and clear images are obtained in relatively short examination times (approximately 4 minutes) (figure 4.31). The fact that no potentially harmful contrast agents need to be injected, such as the iodine or barium used in X-ray imaging techniques, is a great advantage. Indeed, tea and coffee provide excellent contrast in stomach or bladder imaging!

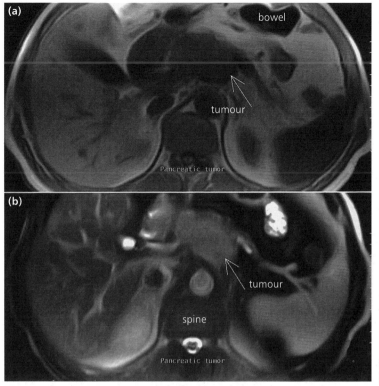

Figure 4.31 Tumour in the pancreas: **(a)** T_1-weighted; **(b)** T_2-weighted.

Flow effects

The magnitude of the MRI signal coming from a *moving* fluid, such as blood, urine or CSF, depends on its previous location in the field. Characteristic *changes* in the MRI signal at a given location can thus give details of fluid velocity, direction and flow pattern.

Magnetic resonance spectroscopy (MRS)

The **hydrogen** nucleus has proved to be the most successful one to image in MRI because it gives the strongest signal and moreover is extremely abundant in the body, in water.

It is, however, possible to image other nuclei with *odd* numbers of protons (giving suitable magnetic properties) notably ^{13}C, ^{19}F, ^{23}Na and ^{31}P. Each type of nucleus has its own characteristic resonant (Larmor) frequency in the radio frequency range, and specific nuclei can thus be 'targeted'.

For example, ^{31}P can be imaged allowing muscular disorders, like

MRI APPLICATIONS

- **Abnormal body water** presence (swelling, infection, bleeding, cysts).
- **Head** and **spine** (tumours, ruptured discs).
- **Joints** (ruptured tendons, worn cartilage).
- **Abdomen** (tumours and diseased tissue in the liver, pancreas, bladder and kidney).
- **Fluid flow** (blocked blood vessels, heart studies).

MRI SAFETY

Since the birth of MRI over 20 years ago, extensive research and clinical evaluations have identified **no adverse biological effects** to those either administering or receiving the examinations. Nevertheless, there are potential hazards in dealing with large and varying magnetic fields, so that strict controls and precautions are necessary. As always, particular care is needed when dealing with pregnant women and young children.

Physiological damage

There are three types of field to consider:

- The large **static field**

Although no biological effects have been observed at flux densities below 2 T, there is evidence that stronger fields can induce small voltages (identified on electrocardiograms) through charges flowing in blood. Some effects reported at these high field strengths include fatigue, headaches, lowered blood pressure, and irritability.

- The time-varying **gradient fields**

Changes in magnetic fields (like the gradient fields being switched on and off) can *induce* currents in conductors, such as the nerves, blood vessels and muscles of the patient. Although no long-term detrimental effects have been reported, rapid variations *can* lead to the sensations of light flashes in the eyes and mild muscular contractions, with the associated risk of heart failure in patients with severe cardiac disease.

- The **radio frequency fields**

The predominant biological effect of rf absorption is local **heating** of body tissue, although in practice this is very small, due to the short pulse duration. It is recommended that body temperature should not rise more than 1°C, but special precautions are necessary when irradiating the eye lens and testes, which cannot dissipate heat very quickly.

Instruments and equipment

Any **magnetic material**, whether inside or outside the body, will be accelerated in the presence of the large magnetic fields of the MRI scanners. Small steel objects, like scissors or scalpels, can be formidable missiles when introduced into the scan room, and even larger objects, such as oxygen cylinders, can be whisked a few metres! Non-magnetic surgical tools have to be carefully selected.

Non-magnetic tools are also required by maintenance staff in the area: a 'spanner in the works' would not be appreciated!

Visitors (and other personnel) are recommended to deposit credit cards, watches, keys and other magnetically sensitive items *outside* the scan room.

Rf coils and their connecting cables inevitably become *hot*, and direct contact with the patient must be avoided to prevent burns.

Special care is required in the handling of the coolants (liquid nitrogen and liquid helium) since these can cause severe burns.

Implants

Foreign objects within the body can not only distort the field, and hence the image, but also they can be hazardous if they are either **magnetic** (iron, steel, cobalt or nickel) or simply **conductive** (any metal).

Magnetic missiles within the body can be life-threatening and careful patient preparation and screening are essential. Surgical clips, metallic fragments (e.g. through industrial accident or in shrapnel) and orthopaedic implants are all potentially dangerous. Eyes are especially at risk. Generally, non-magnetic materials are now employed for implants and can safely be imaged.

Magnetically-sensitive devices, such as cardiac pacemakers and hearing aids, are not permitted in the scan room and warning signs are posted at the relevant entrances.

Conductive (metallic) implants, such as teeth fillings and joint replacements, can have currents *induced* in them by the varying magnetic fields. Induced currents arise mainly through the rapidly varying rf fields, but can also be generated by the switching of the gradient fields and even by patient movement into the main magnetic field. Such currents produce local heating effects, and the examination should be stopped immediately if the patient experiences discomfort. Generally, temperature rises are much less than a degree and present no danger.

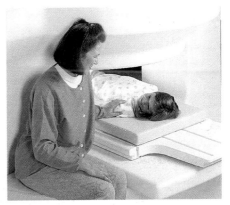

Figure 4.32 A visitor side-chair allows comfort during the examination, and the open nature of the machine reduces claustrophobia.

Patient tolerance

The patient is subjected to a number of possible discomforts:

- **claustrophobia** due to confinement in the bore of the magnet
- large **noise** levels (65–95 dB) mainly due to the switching of the gradient fields (ear plugs can be worn)
- **long** examination times, during which any movement must be avoided.

The more open structure of permanent magnets and recent superconducting models has obvious advantages for claustrophobic patients (figure 4.32). In addition, new coil designs with acoustic shielding have greatly reduced noise levels and improved communication between operator and patient.

ADVANTAGES AND DISADVANTAGES OF MRI

Advantages

1 **Safe** since no ionising radiations are used.
2 **Any selected plane** and orientation can be imaged.
3 Excellent **soft tissue contrast**, no artificial contrast agents are necessary.
4 **Versatile** since image varies with many parameters.
5 Body function and chemistry investigated as well as structure.

Disadvantages

1 High capital and running **costs**.
2 Image selection and interpretation is **complex**.
3 Examination can be **claustrophobic, noisy** and **long**.
4 Hazards with **implants**, particularly pacemakers.
5 Practical problems associated with large superconducting magnets.

Quenching

Quenching refers to the sudden shutdown of the main superconducting magnet by increasing its temperature, thus rendering it resistive instead of superconductive. It may occur through accident or by design, and has several serious consequences.

- The rapid decrease in the magnetic field can induce large currents, causing significant patient heating.
- Irreparable damage can occur to the superconducting coils.
- Helium is boiled off very rapidly, demanding effective venting to the outside environment.

In an emergency shutdown, for example in the case of a fire in the scan room, the field is typically reduced to 50% in 10 s and 99% in 30 s, to protect the patient.

QUESTIONS

Assume $e = 1.6 \times 10^{-19}$ C, $h = 6.63 \times 10^{-34}$ J s, $\dfrac{\gamma}{2\pi}$
for hydrogen nuclei = 42.57 MHz T^{-1}

1 a What is meant by proton
   i spin
   ii precession?
  b Explain carefully why a spinning proton develops its own magnetic field. Describe how the direction of this field changes as the proton precesses.

2 a Explain the terms
   i Larmor frequency
   ii gyromagnetic ratio, γ
  b Calculate the precessional frequency of hydrogen nuclei in magnetic flux densities of
   i 0.5 T
   ii 1.0 T
   iii 1.5 T

3 a Name two reasons why the hydrogen nucleus is the most popular one imaged in MRI.
  b When hydrogen nuclei (protons) are in a strong external magnetic field, they can occupy one of two possible energy states. Describe what these states are, indicating which is the higher energy state.
  c Using your answers to question 2, calculate the difference in energy between the two states in each of the given magnetic flux densities. Give your answer in
   i joules
   ii eV.

4 What does NMR stand for? Explain carefully the role of the three terms involved.

5 a What is the purpose of the magnetic gradient fields employed in MRI? How many are required and why?
  b A patient is positioned horizontally in a steady, uniform horizontal magnetic field of flux density 1 T, running from his feet to his head. If a gradient field of 80 mT m^{-1} is applied horizontally, from his feet to his head, calculate
   i the magnetic flux density 1.3 m from his feet
   ii the frequency of the oscillating magnetic field required to produce proton resonance at this 'slice'.
  c In what range does this frequency lie?

6 a What is meant by relaxation in the context of MRI? Distinguish between transverse and longitudinal relaxation and explain why one is described as a 'recovery' and the other is described as a 'decay'. Why are these of paramount importance in determining the contrast in MRI?

b Compare the appearance of
   i bone
   ii soft tissue
in both an MRI 'proton-density' scan and a conventional 'X-ray'.

7 a The nuclear magnetic resonance (NMR) effect is used for medical imaging. Images are produced from information collected from atoms in the body, particularly hydrogen atoms.
In what sense is the technique **nuclear**?
  b Explain the advantages of NMR over X-rays as an imaging method.
  c NMR requires three separate magnetic fields. Explain the chief function of
   i the strong uniform field
   ii the field gradient supplied by secondary coils
   iii the short pulse magnetic fields which oscillate at radio frequencies.

(ULEAC 1997)

8 a What is meant by resolution? List three ways in which this can be maximised in MRI.
  b Are there any problems associated with your suggestions?

9 a Why is
   i magnetic screening, and
   ii metallic screening
of patients about to undergo an MRI examination necessary?
  b Suggest how such screenings might take place.
  c Design a questionnaire to present to a patient about to undergo an MRI examination, listing six **vital** questions.

10 Contrast and compare the shielding of examination rooms necessary in the following departments:
  a MRI
  b X-ray
  c nuclear medicine.

11 What is
  a a superconducting magnet? Why is it used in MRI?
  b a cryogen? Explain its role in MRI and state what additional problems its use creates.

12 a Suggest three ways in which patient claustrophobia during MRI can be alleviated.
  b Despite the possible uneasiness experienced, the MRI scan can provide unrivalled images of many body structures. Give three examples of situations where MRI is preferable to other imaging modalities.

Radiotherapy and radiological protection

Cancer is currently second only to heart-related disease as the main cause of death in the developed world. A tumour is a mass of abnormally growing (cancer) cells, and it can appear in almost any part of the body. The cancer cells do not respond to the normal mechanisms that control cell growth, and they divide and invade the surrounding tissues. A tumour may split up, releasing small clumps of cells which travel to other parts of the body, where they continue to divide uncontrollably, forming a secondary tumour (figure 5.1).

Radiation therapy, or simply **radiotherapy**, aims to provide effective treatment for cancers by using ionising radiation to destroy diseased tissues, whilst minimising the harm done to healthy cells, and causing as little discomfort to the patient as possible. One of the most common forms of radiotherapy today is **megavoltage therapy**, during which high-energy X-radiation, generated using a **linear accelerator**, is directed into the body, often from several different directions (see figure 5.8). The cumulative effect at the tumour, usually after several treatments, is designed to be lethal.

The **dose** of ionising radiation administered to the patient is *critical*. There is evidence that a variation of 5–10% in absorbed dose can have one of two possible outcomes: too much, and surrounding healthy tissue suffers; too little, and the cancer re-grows. Careful treatment planning is therefore essential for success.

It is perhaps ironic that the very radiation that can help to *destroy* a cancer can also be the *cause* of it. Ionising radiations, including X-radiation, can induce disease in healthy tissue on a scale not initially appreciated by early radiation workers (figure 2.3, page 28). The provision of adequate **radiological protection**, for both patients and medical staff, is crucial, not only in radiotherapy departments, but also in diagnostic units.

These conflicting effects of ionising radiation form the subject of this chapter.

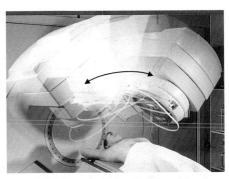

Figure 5.2 A linear accelerator displaying rotational beam therapy.

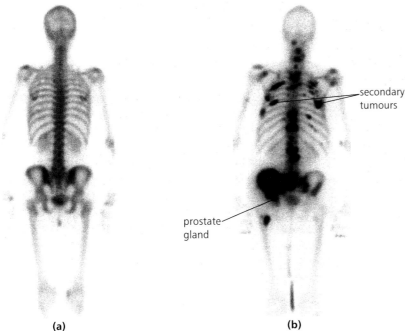

secondary tumours

prostate gland

(a)   (b)

Figure 5.1 Bone scans using a radioactive tracer: **(a)** normal; **(b)** diseased. The original cancer site was in the prostate gland, but widespread secondary tumours are clearly visible.

Tumours – some medical background

In normal living tissue, cells grow, mature, replicate themselves and die. The balance of new cells replaces the old and the organism remains stable. If this cycle is broken so that the cells reproduce at too great a rate, a tumour, which is defined as a mass of abnormal tissue, is produced.

Tumours can be divided into benign and malignant types. Benign tumours usually remain in one place, and often grow quite slowly, sometimes remaining unchanged for many years. Generally, they cause problems only if their growth interferes with the normal working of nearby organs.

Cancer is the name given to a range of diseases where there is a malignant tumour. A malignant tumour may grow slowly for a time and then faster; it infiltrates surrounding structures and will destroy them. Cells can also disperse to other parts of the body where they may begin a new tumour.

Malignant tumours are usually dangerous unless treated, but if detected at an early stage there are various methods by which they may be removed or destroyed. Treatment depends on the nature of the tumour and its location. There are four basic methods, and the treatment for any one patient may involve two or more of them.

- **Surgery** If a tumour is easily located, it may simply be removed.
- **Chemotherapy** The patient is given doses of cell destroying drugs.
- **Hormone therapy** Some hormone-dependent tumours can be treated by altering the hormone balance within the body.
- **Radiotherapy** Tumour cells are destroyed with high-energy radiation, either gamma-rays from a radioactive source (often cobalt-60) or X-rays.

From an article entitled 'X-rays in medicine', *Physics Review*, November 1995.

Ionising radiations – do they kill or cure?

The destruction

Radiation damages cells through **ionisation**. This may be a *direct* ionisation of important molecules, such as **DNA**, in the cell nucleus (figure 5.3), or an *indirect* action through ionisation of the more abundant water molecules within the cell.

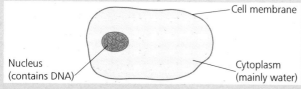

Figure 5.3 A human cell.

DNA is a complex molecule responsible for protein synthesis and growth patterns. Even a small change in the DNA molecule can lead to severe cell changes, known as **mutations**. In some cases, the cell begins to grow uncontrollably (**cancer**), whilst in others its ability to reproduce is destroyed (**sterilisation**).

The ionisation of water molecules results in the formation of the 'free radicals' H and OH. These are very reactive and potentially damaging, often leading to cell death or the onset of mutation.

Cells are most vulnerable to radiation damage when they are reproducing, so that fast growing cells are very **radiation sensitive**, for example the developing fetus, the reproductive organs and bone marrow. In contrast, brain and bone tissues, which do not replace themselves rapidly, are least affected.

The cure

Cancerous cells tend to *reproduce more rapidly* than normal cells, making them relatively more *radiation-sensitive* and capable of being *selectively destroyed* through irradiation. The target is always the DNA within the nucleus: breaks in the DNA strands can result in cell death or loss of reproductive capacity, either of which halts the spread of the disease.

Healthy cells recover from irradiation more quickly than cancer cells. In order to achieve the greatest destruction of cancer cells, with the least damage to surrounding healthy tissue, the radiation should therefore be delivered in short treatments or '**fractions**' of relatively high doses over a period of time. A typical **fractionation scheme** might involve daily treatment, Monday to Friday, for five weeks.

The care

Certain organs in the body are very vulnerable to radiation damage and, during therapy, it is important to keep the dose delivered to these tissues to a minimum. Such **critical organs** include the:

- eye (cataracts)   • reproductive organs (sterility)
- spinal cord (paralysis)   • kidney, liver, rectum.

MEGAVOLTAGE THERAPY (4–25 MV)

Diagnostic X-ray tubes operate at kilovolts (kV) to produce X-rays of the required energy for diagnosis.

In order to generate X-ray beams capable of *destroying* tissue, much higher voltages, in the **megavoltage** (**MV**) range, are necessary, in order to produce photons of higher energies. There are *two* major reasons why these higher energies are needed.

- At lower photon energies (in the keV diagnostic range) attenuation of the X-ray beam is largely through **photoelectric absorption** (see page 40). This depends strongly ($\propto Z^3$) on tissue type, giving the good contrast required in a radiograph. However, this dependence is positively hazardous in therapy! Bone, with its high attenuation, would be at risk, and the dose distribution within the patient would fluctuate enormously from tissue to tissue.

  It is much better to use higher photon energies (in the MeV range), so that attenuation is mainly through **Compton scatter**, which is the same for all tissue types.

- Secondly, the penetration of the beam into tissue increases with photon energy. This allows treatment of deeper sites at higher energies, at the same time as sparing skin tissues (see box below). As a very rough guide, the maximum dose is delivered at a depth (in cm) of 1/4 of the accelerating megavoltage generating the beam. Thus, at 6 MV, the maximum dose is delivered at a tissue depth of 1.5 cm, whilst 16 MV would be required to maximise the dose at 4 cm.

Figure 5.4 A 'plotting tank' of water behaves very much like body tissue and is used to mimic radiation absorption in the body. Radiation monitors in the water map the dose distribution obtained with various beams.

Beam characteristics

The absorption of a therapy beam in a patient's tissues, (figures 5.4 and 5.5), results in a complicated pattern of absorbed dose throughout the body. This can be illustrated by

- absorbed dose along the axis of the beam, (**depth dose**),
- absorbed dose at *right-angles* to the beam axis, (a **beam profile**), or
- a series of beam profiles drawn at different dose values. The lines on this representation join points of equal dose and are therefore called **isodose lines or curves**. They are rather like contour lines on a map and the resulting diagram is known as an **isodose chart**. The numbers on the isodose lines represent the percentage of the maximum dose at any point.

Depth dose

As the energy of the beam increases, there is less reduction of dose with depth. Thus, *higher energy beams are more penetrating*, making them useful for treating deep-sited tumours.

Also, whilst the low-energy X-ray beam delivers its maximum dose at the surface, the higher energy beams result in maximum doses *below* the surface. This is due to the greater range of the forward scattered electrons (from Compton scattering) produced in the first few mm beneath the surface. Such electrons produced thus deliver their energy deeper into the tissues. This effect is known as **skin sparing**, because the dose received by the skin is actually less than that below the surface.

Beam profile

Away from the axis, the absorbed dose decreases rapidly in a region called the '**penumbra**', indicating the sharpness of the beam. This 'penumbra blur' has the same origin as in a diagnostic X-ray tube (see page 43), namely the size of the source, which should therefore be small.

The '**tails**' on the profiles beyond the penumbra are due to the scattering of X-rays out of the primary beam.

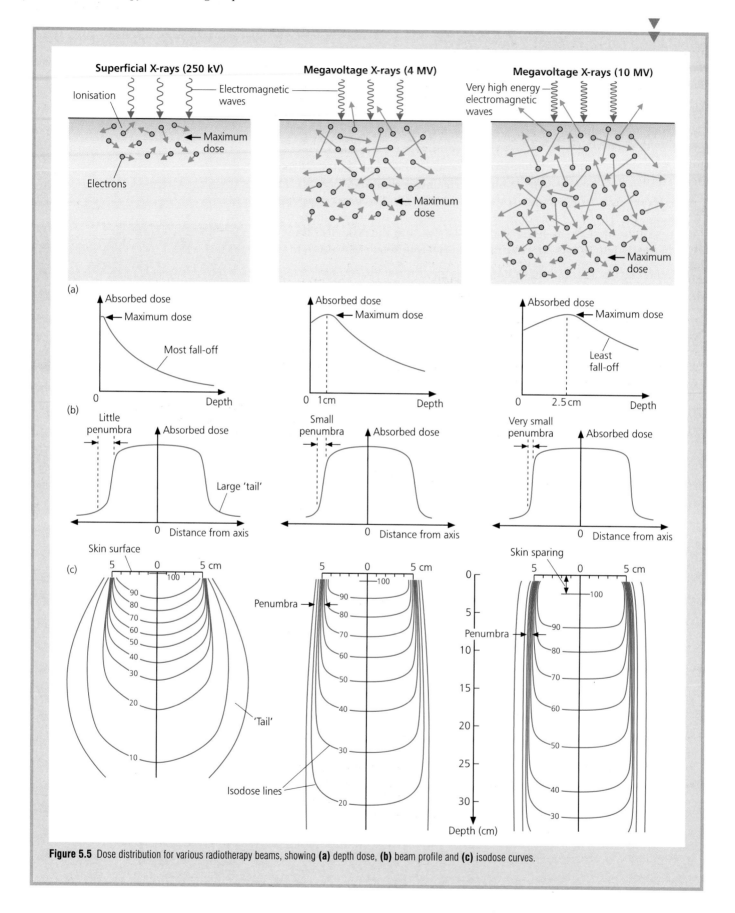

Figure 5.5 Dose distribution for various radiotherapy beams, showing **(a)** depth dose, **(b)** beam profile and **(c)** isodose curves.

Superficial radiotherapy (50–150 kV)

This is used to treat **skin tumours** and aims to deliver a maximum dose to the skin, whilst leaving underlying tissues relatively unharmed. For this reason, lower-energy photons are more suitable, and the beam is usually generated using an X-ray tube. Virtually any field shape or size can be achieved using a lead cut-out, 1 or 2 mm thick, which rests on the patient's skin.

Although superficial X-ray therapy, with its limited tissue penetration, is still used in some centres, it is increasingly being replaced by electron beam therapy, using a linear accelerator.

Multiple and rotational beams

In order to minimise the damage to intervening tissue, a number of low-intensity beams are directed into the patient from different directions (figure 5.6). If they combine at the tumour, the **cumulative dose** there is large enough to destroy the cancer cells, whilst sparing surrounding healthy tissue. This addition of beams can be achieved using

- **multiple beams:** several separate beams are aimed at the tumour from various directions, passing through different parts of the body
- **rotational beams:** a single beam is rotated around the stationary patient, whilst always aiming the beam towards the tumour. This is sometimes called **rotational arc therapy** (see figure 5.2).

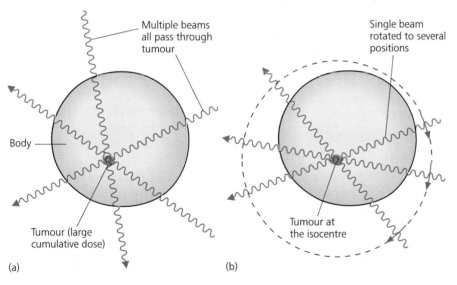

Figure 5.6 Beam delivery: **(a)** multiple beams; **(b)** rotating beams.

The gamma knife

The recently developed 'gamma knife' is a £3 million machine, capable of destroying brain tumours by firing hundreds of fine gamma beams from different directions at a well-defined target area. It is only through accurate three-dimensional imaging, using the modalities described in previous chapters, that the technique has become possible.

Wedges and compensators

Since the body surface is not completely flat, the shape of the radiation field delivered must be modified by the use of shaped absorbers, called **compensators** (figure 5.7(a)). These are individually designed out of wax, or lead foil of different thicknesses, to match the body curves, and essentially correct for the 'missing tissue'.

Furthermore, some tissues within the body absorb radiation better than others, or alternatively are very vulnerable to radiation damage and need extra protection. The shape of the applied field can then be adjusted using a thin lead **wedge** in the path of the beam (figure 5.7(b)), so that it absorbs one side of the beam (where the wedge is thicker) to a greater extent than the other.

Both wedges and compensators retain the skin-sparing effect of high-energy beams, unless they are placed very close to or touching the patient's skin.

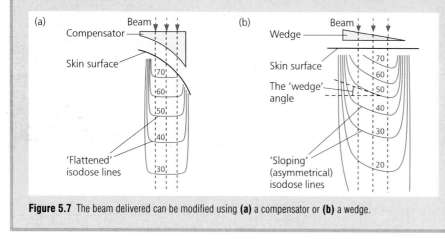

Figure 5.7 The beam delivered can be modified using **(a)** a compensator or **(b)** a wedge.

RADIOTHERAPY

- Destroys cancer cells whilst minimising damage to healthy tissue.
- **Superficial therapy** (~150 kV), destroys **skin tumours**, without harming underlying tissues. It uses an X-ray tube.
- **Megavoltage (MV) therapy**, ($4–25 \times 10^6$ volts), destroys deeper tumours, without harming the skin. It uses a **linear accelerator**.
- Damage to healthy tissue is minimised using **multiple beams rotational beams wedges** and **compensators**.

THE LINEAR ACCELERATOR (LINAC)

To produce the X-rays needed in **megavoltage therapy**, we use the same basic principles as those employed in diagnostic X-ray production, but on a grander scale. Electrons are accelerated through megavoltages (MV) to extremely high energies and then directed to smash into targets, yielding the required very high-energy X-rays. This occurs in a **lin**ear **ac**celerator, or simply **linac**.

In the last 40 years, the linac has developed from the large, cumbersome machine, found mainly in nuclear physics research laboratories, into a compact, standard hospital source of **megavoltage X-rays**. Most major hospital radiotherapy departments will have several such machines, producing a range of low- and high-energy X-ray beams.

In these machines an electron beam is emitted by an **electron gun** through thermionic emission (figure 5.8) just as in a conventional X-ray tube (see page 30). The electrons are accelerated to a velocity approaching that of light along an evacuated tube, as detailed in the box. In order to generate an X-ray beam, the electrons are deflected, usually through 90°, by electromagnets to strike a target. Here, the electrons rapidly decelerate, yielding up their energies to high-energy X-radiation. Since the electron energies involved are so much greater than in an X-ray tube, a **transmission target** is used, whereby X-rays are produced from the far side of the target and directed into the patient.

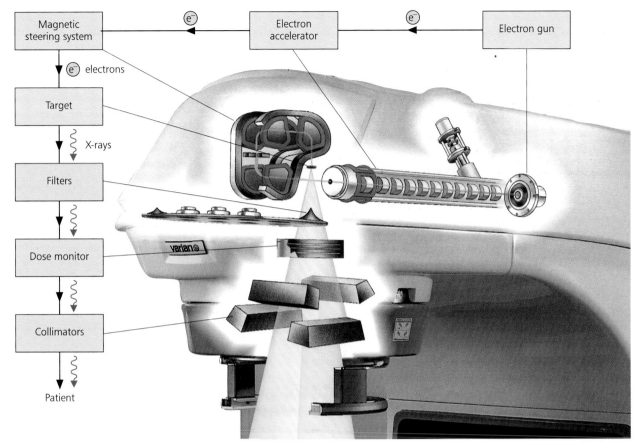

Figure 5.8 The basic components of a hospital linac.

Electron acceleration

Electrons can be accelerated along an evacuated tube by applying a potential difference V across the ends of the tube just as in a conventional X-ray tube. The energy gained by the electron as it accelerates along the tube is then eV joules, or simply V electron-volts. Since electron energies in the MeV range are required in megavoltage therapy, clearly voltages in the MV range are needed across the tube.

Drift tube accelerator

To reduce the insulation problems arising from the application of very large voltages, the tube may be split into sections and an alternating voltage applied across the segments (figure 5.9). The segments themselves, called **drift tubes**, are field-free zones, but an accelerating electric field is experienced by the electrons as they cross the gaps, as long as the polarity of the field is correct. If the segment lengths

and frequency of the applied electric field are carefully chosen to match the electron motion, the electrons will always be accelerated in a series of 'kicks' across the gaps.

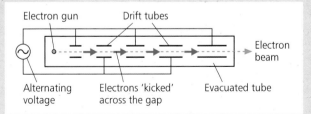

Figure 5.9 Electron acceleration in a drift tube accelerator.

Waveguide accelerator

Instead of applying the accelerating electric field in bursts at a series of electrode gaps, it is possible to provide the electron acceleration using a radio frequency **standing electromagnetic wave** set up in a **waveguide** (see figure 5.8).

The linear accelerator – Worked example

Electrons are accelerated through a series of drift tubes in a linac. There are 20 such tubes and the potential difference across adjacent tubes is 200 kV. Calculate
a) the total voltage through which an electron is accelerated
b) the total energy gained by each electron in i) joules and ii) eV
c) the maximum X-ray photon energy produced. Sketch the photon energy distribution you would expect to get in the output beam, and estimate a typical photon energy delivered in the beam.
d) Why is it necessary for the length of the drift tubes to increase along the accelerator as shown in figure 5.9?
($e = 1.6 \times 10^{-19}$ C).

a) The total voltage is given by

$$19 \times 200\,\text{kV}$$

(There are 20 tubes, but only 19 gaps!)

$$= 3800\,\text{kV}$$
$$= 3.8\,\text{MV}$$

b) i) The energy gained by a single electron is found using

$$\textbf{Energy = charge} \times \textbf{voltage}$$
$$= 1.6 \times 10^{-19}\,\text{C} \times 3.8 \times 10^{6}\,\text{V}$$
$$= 6.1 \times 10^{-13}\,\text{J}\ (2\text{sf})$$

ii) The energy gained in eV is simply 3.8×10^{6} eV, or 3.8 MeV.

c) A photon is emitted with maximum energy when the incident electron gives up *all* of its energy to the photon, in this case 3.8 MeV. Most photons will, however, have less energy than this (figure 5.10). A typical photon energy would be around 2 MeV.

d) The alternating accelerating voltage is reversing in direction at regular time intervals. For synchronisation, the electrons must spend the same amount of time in each drift tube, so that they always arrive at the gap when the field direction is accelerating them. Since their speed is increasing along the length of the linac, the drift tubes must get increasingly longer, so that the *time* spent in them remains the same.

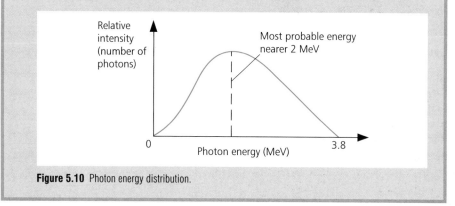

Figure 5.10 Photon energy distribution.

The treatment head

The target (figure 5.11) is normally of high atomic number and thick enough to absorb most of the electrons. The conversion to a high-energy **X-ray beam** is more efficient at these large energies (4–25 MeV) than in the diagnostic X-ray tube.

Lead collimators are used to define and shape the exact field size required and reduce unwanted scatter (or 'leakage') (see box page 107), whilst a **flattening filter** improves uniformity across the field.

Detailed 'sculpting' of the delivered beam is made using metal **wedges**, or **compensators** (see figure 5.7), which improve dose uniformity and protect vital organs from exposure.

A **dose monitor** is incorporated into the head to measure the dose delivered to the patient, and electrically terminates the treatment when the prescribed dose is delivered.

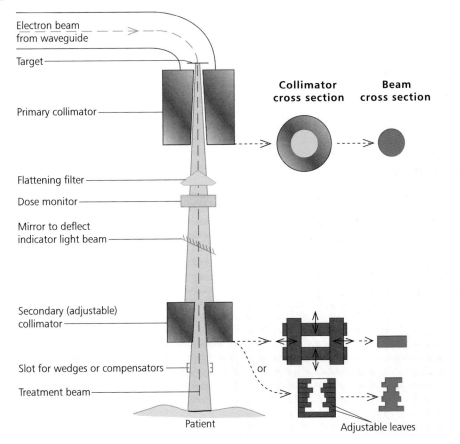

Figure 5.11 The treatment head.

Electron mode

In a **dual-mode** machine, the normal target can be moved out of the path of the electron beam and replaced by a thin scattering foil (low to medium atomic number) to convert the machine into '**electron mode**'. Such a foil 'spreads out' the pencil-thin, focused electron beam to form a broad electron beam of uniform intensity, or **flatness**, for direct delivery to the patient. Since the electron mode is inherently more efficient than X-ray production, the electron-gun current is automatically reduced when the former is selected.

The gantry

The gantry is mounted to rotate about the treatment couch, which is capable of rotation and movement in all three dimensions (figure 5.12). A radiographer feeds the treatment plan, or 'prescription', into a computer, linked to the gantry electronic circuits. During this 'computer-assisted set up', the exact position and orientation of the treatment head with respect to the patient is set, collimators and patient couch are also secured in position, and other accessories such as wedges and compensators are selected (figure 5.13).

Multiple or rotational beams are generally employed and in either case the tumour must be the central target. A simple way of ensuring this is to locate the tumour at the **isocentre** about which everything rotates (see figure 5.6(b)). The linac is constructed so that the isocentre may be contained within a very small volume (of a few mm^3) for all movements of the gantry.

A **rangefinder** is incorporated into the machine to indicate the exact target-to-skin distance (to within 2 mm) along the beam axis.

Alignment devices

The cross-section of the radiation beam delivered to the patient is referred to as the **treatment field**. It is useful to verify the shape, size and position of the treatment field, before treatment, so that accurate delivery of the radiation is ensured.

In order to simulate the radiation beam as closely as possible, an **optical beam** (figure 5.14) can be projected through the system onto the patient, using an angled foil mirror (transparent to X-rays) in the treatment head (see figure 5.11). Other alignment devices include a small **optical video** system or even a low-powered helium-neon **laser beam**.

Finally, a 'picture' of the beam shape superimposed on the patient anatomy can be provided either by an 'on-line' imaging system, using **lower-energy X-rays** in their imaging capacity, or by exposing a fast film with the main beam for a small fraction of the exposure time.

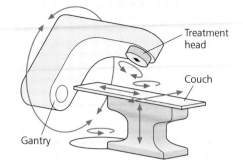

Figure 5.12 Gantry and couch movements: the treatment head can be rotated giving complete flexibility of treatment position.

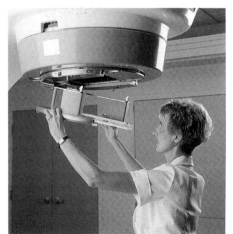

Figure 5.13 Accessories are attached to the treatment head.

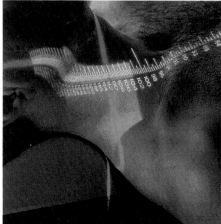

Figure 5.14 Cross-wires, defining the centre of the beam, are useful in aligning the beam to the reference marks made on the patient.

Collimators

The **primary collimator** (see figure 5.11) comprises a large block of lead or heavy alloy, with an aperture shaped to produce a conical beam of circular cross-section.

Traditionally, **secondary collimation** has been provided using adjustable pairs of thick lead blocks, defining variably sized treatment fields of rectangular cross-section. The inner faces of the collimators are angled to align with the beam direction, to ensure sharpness at the edges of the beam.

Collimators must be sufficiently thick to absorb most of the primary beam outside the required treatment field. For the high-energy X-rays now encountered in therapy, as much as 7 cm of lead is needed to reduce the intensity of a beam to below 2% of its initial value.

In order to avoid the use of such large cumbersome collimators, a more flexible system of thin lead 'leaves' is being introduced, known as a **multileaf collimator** (figure 5.15). This is attached directly to the treatment head and consists, for example, of 40 pairs of independently-positioned leaves. It has the great advantage that any irregular field can be delivered by the specific choice of leaf combination.

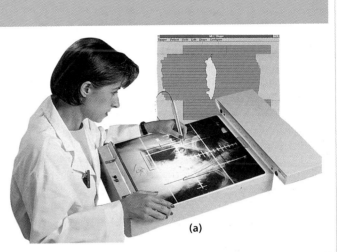

(a)

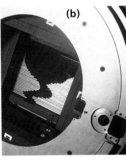

(b)

Figure 5.15 (a) The tumour is electronically outlined and the computer automatically shapes the multileaf collimator to match. **(b)** The multileaf collimator in the treatment head is set ready for treatment.

Cobalt-60 machines

Instead of using high-energy X-ray beams produced by linacs, γ-rays from a radioactive source can also be directed into a patient to treat a cancer.

The most commonly used source in the above applications is ^{60}Co, which has several advantages:

- long half-life (5.3 years) avoids frequent renewal
- convenient γ-ray energy (approximately 1.25 MeV, equivalent to the X-radiation from a 3 MV linac)
- small, concentrated sources, permit short exposure times.

In a cobalt therapy unit (or 'bomb') great care has to be taken to shield the high-activity cobalt source at all times, since it is decaying spontaneously and *cannot be switched off* (unlike the linac).

The permanent radiation risk of a cobalt therapy unit, together with other disadvantages like poorer beam definition and lower patient throughput, has led to most cobalt-60 units being replaced by linacs, except in locations where the maintenance costs of a linac are prohibitive.

LINEAR ACCELERATOR

- An **electron beam** is accelerated in a drift tube or waveguide accelerator, strikes a **transmission target**, is decelerated, producing **X-radiation**.
- **Beam shaping** and **alignment** takes place in the **treatment head**: **lead collimators** define the **treatment field**, **wedges** and **compensators** allow for uneven body shapes and **protect vital organs**, **optical beam to** check the treatment beam position.
- Computer-controlled **gantry** and treatment couch provide any treatment position.
- A **dose monitor** in the treatment head monitors patient dose.

TREATMENT PLANNING

The once lengthy and laborious task of treatment planning has been transformed by the computer into a faster, more flexible operation and opened up horizons in three-dimensional planning that were unheard of a few years ago. The prime objective is to map the exact **dose distribution** *required* in the patient and match it to that *actually produced* by the ionising beams employed, whilst always sparing intermediate and surrounding healthy tissue.

The doctor

The doctor, or **radiotherapist**, analyses information about the size and position of the tumour using the various imaging techniques available, often a combination of an X-ray, a CT scan and an MRI scan. Even ultrasound scanning is sometimes employed, for example in assessing the thickness of the chest wall when planning breast treatments.

The total quantity of radiation required to destroy the tumour depends on many factors, such as

- type of cell irradiated (some cancer cells are more radiation-sensitive than others)
- environment of the cell (its blood and oxygen supply are important)
- extent of the cancer
- fractionation scheme selected (see box page 98) (a larger total dose is needed for more, smaller fractions).

The exact location of the tumour is identified, an 'ideal' dose to destroy it is chosen and notes are made concerning a suitable fractionation scheme and the protection of surrounding healthy tissue.

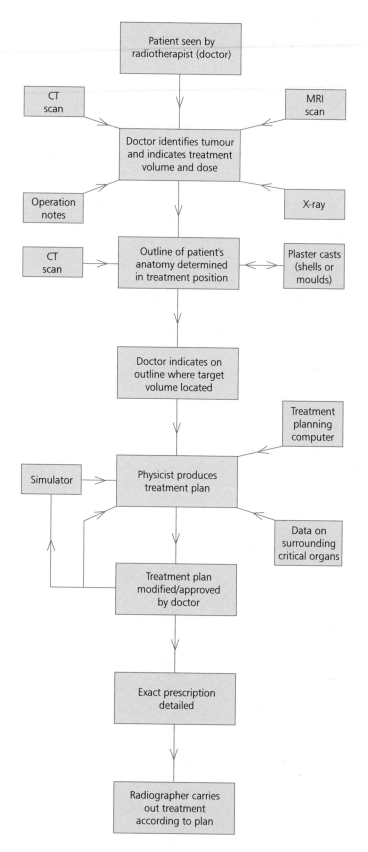

Figure 5.16 A number of highly-specialised medical staff are involved in treatment planning.

The medical physicist

The medical physicist then *plans how to deliver* the required dose distribution by considering:

- number and directions of beams (fields) to be used and whether they are multiple or rotational
- field sizes
- source-to-skin distance (SSD) for each field
- 'weighting factors' (i.e. relative dose) of each field
- type and orientation of wedges and compensators needed to protect critical organs.

Imaging data acquired by the radiotherapist, together with information from the **simulator** (see box) allows the computer to present a detailed two-dimensional cross-section of the relevant body sector, together with an outline of the target area (the tumour). The fields are selected and the computer rapidly calculates the summed doses received at a large number of points within the displayed slice. Isodose curves are then superimposed onto the patient's anatomy (figure 5.17) to form the **first plan**. Ultimately, the aim is to get the 95% isodose curve to enclose the tumour or 'target' area, whilst ensuring a uniform dose distribution (<5% variation) across the tumour area.

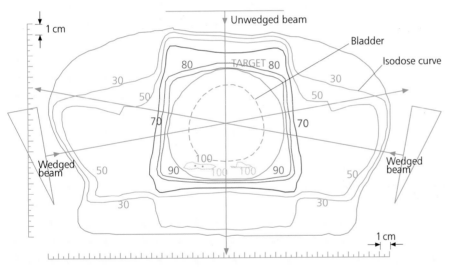

Figure 5.17 A bladder treatment plan – commonly the first plan is not ideal and needs modifying.

The medical physicist may then wish to modify the fields further to protect **critical organs**, such as the gonads, lungs or rectum from irradiation. In consultation with the radiotherapist a final **treatment plan**, or **prescription**, is agreed and then dispatched to the **radiographer** for treatment.

Isodose curves

An **isodose curve** is a line, drawn on a dose distribution chart, joining points of equal dose in the patient. It is rather like a contour line on a map, linking points of equal height, and for this reason, it is sometimes called an isodose contour. The number on an **isodose curve** represents the percentage of the maximum dose at any point.

The simulator

Before a course of treatment starts, the patient attends a simulator, which duplicates the treatment machine set-up, with the major omission of the treatment beam! It helps to 'visualise' and adjust the position of the final beam with respect to the patient's anatomy.

A simulator is essentially a specialised diagnostic X-ray machine, which is capable of copying (or simulating) all the movements and adjustment features of the actual treatment machine. Associated equipment, like the patient couch, is also identical to the treatment situation, so that a 'trial run' through the simulator, using low-energy imaging X-rays, is indeed a fair representation of the 'real thing'.

In place of the collimators used in the therapy machine, a grid of fine field-defining wires is employed. The image of these wires is superimposed on the image of the patient's anatomy, allowing field sizes to be set and checked.

THE TREATMENT

Before the first treatment, indelible marks (or 'tattoos') may be drawn on the patient's skin to identify the exact treatment area. These are not removed until the final treatment is complete. It is possible that additional casts or moulds have to be made, for example to support the head and neck in a stationary position and these are re-used at each session.

The patient is carefully positioned on the treatment couch (an exercise that often takes longer than the treatment itself) and alignment of the beam is checked optically. The radiographer then leaves the room whilst treatment is in progress, and observes the patient by audio-visual monitor. (A 10-minute stay in the treatment room on average would give the radiographer the maximum permitted **annual** dose.)

During exposure, the patient needs to keep as still as possible, although swallowing and breathing are still permitted!

Careful monitoring of dose is essential throughout the treatment. Not only are monitors incorporated into the treatment machine, to measure output, but also the dose *received* by the patient is estimated from dosimeters either on or in the patient. Cumulative dose can be recorded by using the same dosimeters at each treatment.

Side effects

These vary enormously from patient to patient and of course depend on the nature of the treatment. Possible side effects reported include tiredness, depression, nausea, skin irritation (rather like sunburn) and hair loss. These are all temporary conditions, even if very unpleasant at the time, and patients need considerable support from both medical staff and family during such treatments.

Other radiotherapy techniques

In addition to the conventional external beam radiotherapy described so far, there are two other methods available for delivering destructive ionising radiations to a cancerous area.

- **Radioactive implants**, such as iridium-192, are inserted into body tissues such as the breast, using fine wires or needles, or into body cavities, such as the uterus.

- **Radionuclide therapy** involves administering a destructive (usually β- or low-energy γ-emitting) radionuclide into the body, so that it will preferentially accumulate in the target area (e.g. high-dose ^{131}I in the thyroid gland).

APPLICATIONS OF RADIOTHERAPY

The use of radiotherapy in **oncology** (that branch of medicine that deals with tumours) is widespread.

Bladder and prostate

This is a common treatment (see figure 5.17). Since the size and position of the bladder walls vary with the volume of urine in the bladder, it is important that the bladder is emptied within 5–10 minutes of treatment, to ensure identical tumour location at each treatment.

Breast

Two opposed (at 180°) wedged fields are commonly used to minimise radiation damage to the underlying lung (figure 5.18).

Cervix, uterus and vagina

Cancer of the cervix and uterus is normally treated using a combination of external beams and implants. The treatment plan must protect the nearby critical organs, the rectum, bladder and bowel and the treatment requires a general or local anaesthetic. Vaginal treatments need no anaesthetic and can be dealt with on an out-patient basis.

Chest

Lung cancer is one of the major causes of death from cancer. In the majority of cases it is caused by the exposure to cigarette smoke. Careful treatment planning is necessary to achieve a high dose to the tumour, whilst sparing the heart and spinal cord, as well as healthy lung tissue. External wedged rotational beams are usually employed.

Head and neck

Purpose-built shells or moulds, shaped to match the exact patient contours, are used to minimise patient movement. Beam entry marks can then be made on the shell, avoiding the need for indelible marks to be made on the patient's face or neck. Critical organs, like the eye and spinal cord, must be protected using suitably shaped fields.

Brain tumours and blood vessel malformations are usually treated using narrow rotational beams delivering a high dose to a small target volume in a single fraction. Such treatment is precise and effective.

Skin

Skin tumours may be treated using low-energy (superficial) X-rays, electron beams, or surface implants.

Total body irradiation (TBI)

When a condition affects the entire body, as for example in leukaemia (too many white corpuscles in the blood) treatment of the whole body is required. Sometimes, high-dose treatments are recommended, for example to eradicate fully the patient's diseased bone marrow prior to bone marrow transplantation. Otherwise, lower dose treatments, involving large fields, are employed.

RADIOLOGICAL PROTECTION

The purpose of radiation or **radiological protection** is to provide a good standard of safety for people exposed to ionising radiation, without unduly limiting its uses.

In the hospital, there are many different sectors of the community to protect: the general public (people visiting, delivering and so on) the medical team, working daily either directly or indirectly with ionising radiation, and of course the patient! Strict codes of practice are drawn up to implement the basic principles of radiological protection, and to control and monitor radiation exposure.

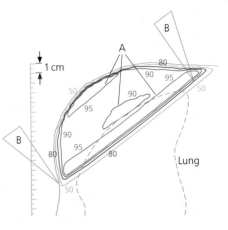

Figure 5.18 Breast treatment plan.

RADIOTHERAPY TREATMENT

- Aims to destroy the tumour, whilst sparing healthy tissue.
- **Treatment plan** defines number, size, direction and strength of beams, **fractionation** scheme, **wedges** and **compensators**.
- **Treatment** demands accurate **positioning** and minimal **movement** of the patient, careful **dose monitoring**.
- **Applied dose** is **critical**.
- **Side effects** include tiredness, depression, nausea, skin irritation and hair loss.
- **Diseases treated** include leukaemia, and cancer in the bladder, breast, lung, head and skin.

General practical points

- Areas where work with ionising radiation is carried out are designated and clearly marked as *controlled areas* to which access is limited (figure 5.19).
- Regular quality assurance checks are made of all relevant equipment.
- Radiation protection monitors are worn by all relevant personnel, and checked regularly (figure 5.20). *All* incidents of higher than expected doses are investigated.
- Personnel distance themselves as much as possible from sources, by applying the **inverse square law** to reduce the intensity of the radiation received.

Figure 5.19 The internationally agreed yellow and black radiation trefoil indicates a controlled area.

Film badge filters

The film is partially covered with filters of different materials (plastic, aluminium, copper, lead) and thicknesses (figure 5.21).

- Under the open area, the film measures the total dose.
- The film under the plastic filters, when compared with that under the open window, indicates the presence of β-radiation of different energies. (No β-radiation penetrates the metal filters.)
- Aluminium and copper filters will stop low-energy X-rays, but not high-energy X- and γ-rays, which *are* stopped by the lead filters. A comparison of the aluminium and lead filters thus distinguishes between low- and high-energy electromagnetic radiation.
- Emulsions of different sensitivities are used to record a range of doses. The sensitive emulsion (fast film) monitors small doses, whilst, if this emulsion is blackened too heavily, the slower emulsion registers larger doses.

The film badge provides a cheap, permanent record of exposure, and mixed radiation can be determined from one film. On the other hand, it has limited accuracy (10–20%) and there is some delay before the exposure is known.

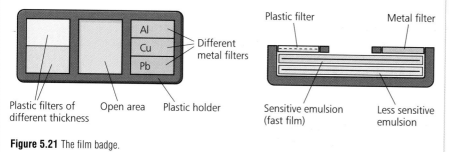

Different metal filters

Plastic filters of different thickness — Open area — Plastic holder

Plastic filter — Metal filter

Sensitive emulsion (fast film) — Less sensitive emulsion

Figure 5.21 The film badge.

Basic principles of radiological protection

Justification No practice involving radiation exposure should be adopted unless its introduction produces a positive net benefit. (Are routine chest X-rays beneficial?)

Optimisation All exposures should be kept As Low As Reasonably Achievable (ALARA) bearing in mind economic and social factors. (Should a particular patient have a CT or MRI brain scan?)

Limitation The effective dose to individuals should not exceed the recommended limits. (Where does therapy stop?)

Figure 5.20 The film badge dosimeter is worn by medical personnel to measure their exposure to radiation. It uses the blackening of photographic film by ionising radiation, and employs various filters over the film to identify the type of radiation present.

The radiography department

- The walls of X-ray rooms are thick enough to limit the transmission of radiation. (100 mm of concrete is sufficient for diagnostic rooms.)
- X-ray rooms are designed so that the primary beam is directed away from adjacent occupied areas.
- The radiographer stands when possible behind a lead glass screen during exposure of the patient (figure 5.22).
- Lead gloves, aprons or sheets are used to restrict the exposure to both patient and radiographer.
- Except in special cases, a minimum filtration of the X-ray beam is used (1.5 mm of aluminium up to 70 kV, 2.5 mm above 70 kV) to reduce dose due to useless low-energy photons.
- Exposure times are kept to a minimum, consistent with the purpose of the investigation.
- Beam definers and collimators are employed to limit the spread of the X-ray beam.
- Intensifying screens are used to increase film sensitivity and thus reduce exposure times.

The nuclear medicine department

- Radionuclides are handled in a specially designed laboratory, containing such features as smooth, non-absorbent, washable surfaces (to deal with contamination), strong benches (to support lead shielding) and sinks employing elbow-operated taps.
- Fans and a small negative pressure ensure the removal of air-borne radiation out of the building.
- Fume cupboards are used to produce and store radiopharmaceuticals.
- Radioactive waste is discharged in a controlled, approved way. (This can also include biological waste from patients to whom radionuclides have been administered!)
- Protective clothing, particularly gloves, overalls and overshoes, is worn by personnel (figure 3.4 on page 55).
- Long-handled tongs are used to manipulate sources, thereby avoiding direct contact and applying the inverse square law for extra protection.
- Finger radiation monitors can be worn by workers frequently involved with tracer preparations.
- Wall-mounted standard radiation detectors monitor local radiation levels.

The radiotherapy department

- Medical personnel leave the treatment room whilst treatment is in progress.
- Safety interlocks are installed on the doors, switching the machine off automatically should the door be opened.
- The treatment room is provided with adequate **lead** shielding.
- The treatment plan is carefully devised to minimise unnecessary exposure, and protect critical organs.
- X-ray beams are accurately collimated and treatment fields restricted to ensure minimum exposure of healthy tissue.
- X-ray energies are selected to give the required penetration, whilst sparing the skin.
- Dose monitors are employed to measure the dose not only delivered by the machine but also received by the patient.

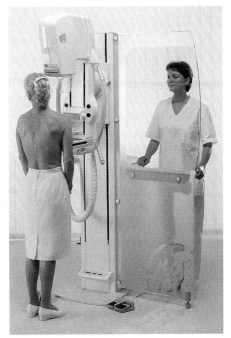

Figure 5.22 A typical breast-screening unit. The lead in the glass is a good absorber of X-rays and protects the radiographer from receiving cumulative radiation doses.

QUESTIONS

1 Describe briefly the processes known as
   a photoelectric absorption
   b Compton scatter
   in X-ray interaction with matter. Explain which process is most important in
      i diagnostic radiography
      ii radiotherapy.
   c Give two reasons why the X-ray photons used in radiotherapy have higher energies than those used in radiography.

2 a Explain what is meant by
      i superficial therapy
      ii megavoltage therapy.
   b State two advantages that megavoltage therapy offers over superficial therapy, and give one application of each.

3 a Describe the similarities and differences in
      i the methods of production
      ii the patterns of absorbed dose in tissue between beams of X-radiation of energies of about 250 kV and 4 MV.
   b Name two devices that can be placed in the beam path to shape the treatment field.

4 a Outline the major components of a linear accelerator, used for producing high-energy X-radiation of maximum photon energy 8 MeV, explaining carefully the energy exchanges occurring at each stage.
   b Describe, with the aid of a sketch graph, the distribution of photon energies in the output beam.
   c If the electrons are accelerated through a series of 25 drift tubes, calculate the voltage across adjacent tubes.

5 a Explain the following terms used in radiotherapy
      i isodose chart
      ii compensator
      iii critical organ.
   b Describe the techniques used in order to spare the skin from excessive radiation doses during megavoltage therapy.

6 Figure 5.18 on page 111 shows a treatment plan for a patient with breast cancer.
   a State the name given to the curves labelled A. Explain the meaning of the numbers on them.
   b Give the name of the components labelled B. What is their purpose, and of what material are they usually made?
   c How many treatment beams are being used here? On a rough sketch, indicate its/their direction(s).
   d Which regions of tissue need protecting here? How well does the treatment plan achieve this?

7 a State two important differences between the ideal radionuclides administered during imaging and therapy.
   b Iodine-131 is a radionuclide used in both procedures. Describe one example of its application in imaging, and one in therapy. Suggest why its use in imaging is rapidly declining in favour of other radionuclides, such as technetium-99m.

8 a Explain what is meant by a treatment plan and outline the procedures adopted in order to achieve an acceptable one. Your answer should contain references to the following terms:
   target volume, isodose curve, critical organ, fractionation scheme, multiple or rotational beams, wedge, compensator, simulator.
   b Why is the final choice of absorbed dose delivered described as being '**critical**'?

9 Not only the patient but also the medical staff may be exposed to ionising radiations in the course of a radiotherapy treatment. Describe two ways in which
   a the patient, and
   b the medical staff
   can be protected from unnecessary exposure.

10 X-rays are used in the treatment of malignancy. Describe a method by which X-ray exposure of healthy tissue surrounding a deep-seated tumour may be minimised.

(UCLES 1996)

11 a X-rays used for diagnosis are generated with tube voltages of around 70 kV compared with several megavolts when X-rays are needed for therapy. What is the difference between diagnosis and therapy?
   b Explain why 70 kV is enough for diagnosis but up to several megavolts is often needed for therapy.

(ULEAC 1997)

12 a In the UK in 1988 the average annual dose of radiation of natural origin was 2000 μSv, where the sievert (Sv) is a unit of radiation dose. Explain why a person living in a region of granite rocks, or at high altitude, receives a dose of background radiation somewhat higher than the average.
   b Concern has been expressed about the effect on radiation dose of draught proofing brick-built, centrally-heated houses. Why might the dose increase in these circumstances?

(ULEAC 1994)

13 a Describe the types of effect which may be produced when the human body is subjected to ionising radiation. Your answer should include
      i microscopic effects and their consequences
      ii macroscopic effects and
      iii an explanation of why the hazard varies with the type of radiation used.
   b Discuss the main sources of radiation dosage which a person living in Britain may receive.
   c Describe the principle of action of **one** radiation detector indicating
      i the type(s) of radiation for which it is suitable and
      ii the type of situation or location in which it could be used.

(OCEAC 1996)

Index

Answers

Note that numerical answers only are given.

ANSWERS TO END-OF-CHAPTER QUESTIONS

Chapter 1
Questions misnumbered in this chapter. Maria Kettle Winkler

4 b (i) $0.0048\,\mathrm{W\,m^{-2}}$
    (ii) $0.9952\,\mathrm{W\,m^{-2}}$
5 $10.5\,\mathrm{cm}$
6 d $18.0\,\mathrm{cm}$
8 a $0.136\,\mathrm{ms^{-1}}$
9 Volume flow rate $= 0.5 \times 10^{-6}\,\mathrm{m^3\,s^{-1}}$
    (Blood flow velocity $= 0.447\,\mathrm{m\,s^{-1}}$)
10 a Frequency (minimum)
    $= 5.2\,\mathrm{MHz}$

4 b $60\,\mathrm{MW\,m^{-2}}$
5 b (i) $3.75\,\mathrm{MW\,m^{-2}}$
    (ii) $2.98\,\mathrm{MW\,m^{-2}}$
6 b (i) $5.0\,\mathrm{kW\,m^{-2}}$
    (ii) $0.45\,\mathrm{m}$
7 b (i) $0.289\,\mathrm{mm^{-1}}$
    (ii) $6.6\,\mathrm{mm}$
    (iii) $126\,\mathrm{kW\,m^{-2}}$
8 b $102\,\mathrm{MW\,m^{-2}}$
9 c 0.63

9 b (i) 4.0×10^6
    (ii) 61
    (iii) 0.0153 (about 1.5%)
11 b $6000\,\mathrm{cm^3}$

Chapter 4

2 b (i) $21.29\,\mathrm{MHz}$
    (ii) $42.57\,\mathrm{MHz}$
    (iii) $63.86\,\mathrm{MHz}$
3 c (i) $1.41 \times 10^{-26}\,\mathrm{J}$
    (i) $8.82 \times 10^{-8}\,\mathrm{eV}$
    (ii) $2.82 \times 10^{-26}\,\mathrm{J}$
    (ii) $1.76 \times 10^{-7}\,\mathrm{eV}$
    (iii) $4.23 \times 10^{-26}\,\mathrm{J}$
    (iii) $2.64 \times 10^{-7}\,\mathrm{eV}$
5 b (i) $1.104\,\mathrm{T}$
    (ii) $47.0\,\mathrm{MHz}$ (radiofrequency)

Chapter 2

1 b (i) $80\,000\,\mathrm{eV}$ ($80\,\mathrm{keV}$)
    (ii) $1.28 \times 10^{-14}\,\mathrm{J}$
2 b Tube voltage $= 62.2\,\mathrm{kV}$
    (maximum photon frequency
    $= 1.5 \times 10^{19}\,\mathrm{Hz}$)
3 b (i) $19.5\,\mathrm{kW}$
    (ii) $1.88 \times 10^{18}\,\mathrm{s^{-1}}$
    (iii) $19.38\,\mathrm{kW}$
    (iv) $0.117\,\mathrm{kW}$

Chapter 3

1 b $0.347\,\mathrm{h^{-1}}$
2 b (i) $0.347\,\mathrm{min^{-1}}$
    (ii) $2.83\,\mathrm{min}$
3 b (i) 0.11
    (ii) $1.4 \times 10^{12}\,\mathrm{Bq}$
4 a $15.6\,\mathrm{days}$
5 a $^{23}_{11}\mathrm{Na} + ^{1}_{0}\mathrm{n} \rightarrow ^{24}_{11}\mathrm{Na} + \gamma$
  b $^{131m}_{52}\mathrm{Te} \rightarrow ^{131}_{53}\mathrm{I} + ^{0}_{-1}\beta + \bar{\nu}$
6 a $^{208}_{81}\mathrm{Tl} \rightarrow ^{208}_{82}\mathrm{Pb} + ^{0}_{-1}\beta + \bar{\nu}$

Chapter 5

4 c $333\,\mathrm{kV}$

Heinemann Educational Publishers
Halley Court, Jordan Hill, Oxford, OX2 8EJ
a division of Reed Educational & Professional Publishing Ltd
Heinemann is a registered trademark of Reed Educational & Professional Publishing Ltd

OXFORD MELBOURNE AUCKLAND
JOHANNESBURG BLANTYRE GABORONE
IBADAN PORTSMOUTH NH (USA) CHICAGO

© Jean Pope, 1999

First published 1999

ISBN 0 435 57094 3

03 02 01 00 99

10 9 8 7 6 5 4 3 2 1

Edited by Donna Evans
Designed and typeset by Gecko Ltd, Bicester, Oxon
Illustrated by Harvey Collins, Mike Parsons
Cover design by Gecko Ltd, Bicester, Oxon
Printed and bound in Spain by Edelvives

Acknowledgements

The authors and Publishers would like to thank the following for permission to use the photographs:

Cover photo by Derriford Hospital, Plymouth; (inset) GE Medical Systems.

I.1a Derriford Hospital, Plymouth; **b** BBC; **c** UCL; **d** Siemens; **1.1a** Dr D Banerjee; **b & c** Derriford Hospital; **1.3** Acuson; **1.8** UCL; **1.11a** Derriford Hospital; **b** UCL; **1.14** UCL; **1.17** Derriford Hospital; **1.18** UCL; **1.19** Derriford Hospital; **1.20** GE Medical Systems; **1.24–1.27** Derriford Hospital; **1.28** Acuson; **2.1** Derriford Hospital; **2.2** UCL; **2.5b** Derriford Hospital; **2.17** UCL; **2.18** Derriford Hospital; **2.19b** UCL; **2.22a** Derriford Hospital; **2.23** Derriford Hospital; **2.24** Science Photo Library; **2.25** Derriford Hospital; **3.1** Derriford Hospital; **3.3a** CIS (UK) Ltd; **3.4, 3.6, 3.7** Derriford Hospital; **3.8–3.9** Elscint (GB) Ltd; **3.11** GE Medical Systems; **3.17–3.18** Derriford Hospital; **3.20–3.21** UCL; **4.1** Derriford Hospital; **4.14** UCL; **4.17** J Pope; **4.18** Derriford Hospital; **4.19a** Siemens; **4.19b, 4.21** J Pope; **4.26** Siemens; **4.27–4.28** GE Medical Systems; **4.29–4.31** Derriford Hospital; **4.32** GE Medical Systems; **5.1** Derriford Hospital; **5.2** Elekta; **5.4** Varian; **5.8** Elektra Oncology Systems; Figure **5.11** based on a brochure from Elekta; **5.13–5.15** Varian; **5.22** GE Medical Systems.

The author and publishers would like to thank the following examination boards for the permission to reproduce their material:

London Examinations, A division of Edexcel Foundation; Northern Examinations and Assessment Board; and University of Cambridge Local Examinations Syndicate for questions on pages 27, 47, 71, 96, 114.

The publishers have made every effort to trace the copyright holders, but if they have inadvertently overlooked any, they will be pleased to make the necessary arrangements at the first opportunity.